Discovering
Geometry
An Investigative Approach

Practice Your Skills
with Answers

DISCOVERING

MATHEMATICS

 **Key Curriculum Press**
Innovators in Mathematics Education

Project Editor: Heather Dever

Editorial Assistant: Erin Gray

Writers: David Rasmussen, Ralph Bothe, Judy Hicks, Michael Serra

Accuracy Checker: Dudley Brooks

Production Editor: Angela Chen

Copyeditor: Margaret Moore

Editorial Production Manager: Deborah Cogan

Production Director: Diana Jean Parks

Production Coordinator: Ann Rothenbuhler

Text Designers: Jenny Somerville, Garry Harman

Art Editor: Jason Luz

Composition, Technical Art: Interactive Composition Corporation

Art and Design Coordinator: Caroline Ayres

Cover Designer: Jill Kongabel

Printer, Prepress: Data Reproductions

Executive Editor: Casey FitzSimons

Publisher: Steven Rasmussen

Key Curriculum Press
1150 65th Street
Emeryville, CA 94608
510-595-7000
editorial@keypress.com
http://www.keypress.com

Printed in the United States of America
10 9 8 7 6 5 4 3   06 05 04   ISBN 1-55953-594-6

Contents

Chapter 10

Chapter 11

Chapter 12

Chapter 13

Introduction

The author and editors of *Discovering Geometry: An Investigative Approach* are aware of the importance of students developing geometry skills along with acquiring concepts through investigation. The student book includes many skill-based exercises. These *Practice Your Skills* worksheets provide problems similar to the exercises in *Discovering Geometry*. Like those exercises, these worksheets allow students to practice and reinforce the important procedures and skills developed in the lessons. Some of these problems provide non-contextual skills practice. Others give students an opportunity to apply geometry concepts in fairly simple, straightforward contexts. Some are more complex problems that are broken down into small steps.

You might assign the *Practice Your Skills* worksheet for every lesson, or only for those lessons your students find particularly difficult. Or you may wish to assign the worksheets on an individual basis, only to those students who need extra help. One worksheet has been provided for nearly every lesson. There are no worksheets for Chapter 0, and the optional tessellation lessons have been combined into one worksheet. To save you the time and expense of copying pages, you can give students the inexpensive *Practice Your Skills Student Workbook,* which does not have answers. Though the copyright allows you to copy pages from *Practice Your Skills with Answers* for use with your students, the consumable *Practice Your Skills Student Workbook* should not be copied.

Lesson 1.1 • Building Blocks of Geometry

Name _____ Period _____ Date _____

For Exercises 1–7, complete each statement. $\overline{PS} = 3$ cm.

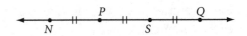

1. The midpoint of $\overline{PQ}$ is _____.

2. $NQ =$ _____.

3. Another name for $\overline{NS}$ is _____.

4. S is the _____ of $\overrightarrow{SQ}$.

5. P is the midpoint of _____.

6. $\overline{NS} \cong$ _____.

7. Another name for $\overrightarrow{SN}$ is _____.

8. Name all pairs of congruent segments in $KLMN$. Use the congruence symbol to write your answer.

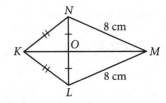

For Exercises 9 and 10, use a ruler to draw each figure. Label the figure and mark the congruent parts.

9. $\overline{AB}$ and $\overline{CD}$ with M as the midpoint of both $\overline{AB}$ and $\overline{CD}$. $AB = 6.4$ cm and $CD = 4.0$ cm. A, B, and C are not collinear.

10. $\overleftrightarrow{AB}$ and $\overline{CD}$. C is the midpoint of $\overline{AB}$ with $AC = 2.5$ cm. D, not on $\overleftrightarrow{AB}$, is the midpoint of $\overline{AE}$, with $AD = 2BC$.

11. $M(-4, 8)$ is the midpoint of $\overline{DE}$. D has coordinates $(6, 1)$. Find the coordinate of E.

12. Sketch six points A, B, C, D, E, and F, no three of which are collinear. Name the lines defined by these points. How many lines are there?

13. Sketch six points U, V, W, X, Y, and Z, on four lines such that each line contains three points. How many lines are concurrent at each point?

14. In the figure at right, $\{B, C, H, E\}$ is a set of four coplanar points. Name two other sets of four coplanar points. How many sets of four coplanar points are there?

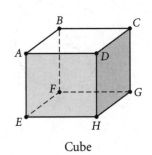

Cube

Lesson 1.2 • Poolroom Math

Name _____ **Period** _____ **Date** _____

For Exercises 1–5, use the figure at right to complete each statement.

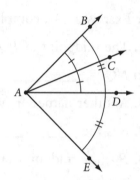

1. A is _____ of ∠BAE.

2. $\overrightarrow{AD}$ is _____ of ∠BAE.

3. $\overrightarrow{AD}$ is _____ of ∠DAE.

4. If $m\angle BAC = 42°$, then $m\angle CAE =$ _____.

5. ∠DAB ≅ _____.

For Exercises 6–10, use your protractor to find the measure of each angle to the nearest degree.

6. $m\angle PRO$ **7.** $m\angle ORT$

8. $m\angle O$ **9.** $m\angle RTO$

10. $m\angle ATO$

For Exercises 11–13, use your protractor to draw and then label each angle with the given measure.

11. $m\angle MNO = 15°$ **12.** $m\angle RIG = 90°$ **13.** $m\angle z = 160°$

For Exercises 14–16, find the measure of the angle formed by the hands at each time.

14. 3:00 **15.** 4:00 **16.** 3:30

17. What's wrong with this statement? "$\overrightarrow{PQ}$ is the angle bisector of ∠APB and $m\angle APQ = 107°$."

18. As P revolves once clockwise around circle O, describe how $m\angle AOP$ changes.

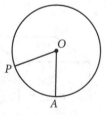

Discovering Geometry Practice Your Skills
©2003 Key Curriculum Press

Lesson 1.3 • What's a Widget?

Name _____ **Period** _____ **Date** _____

For Exercises 1–12, match each term with one of the items (a to l) below.

a.
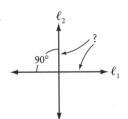

b.

c.
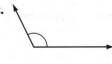

d. $m\angle P = 68°$
$m\angle XYZ = 114°$
$m\angle Y = 112°$
$m\angle STP = 58°$

e.
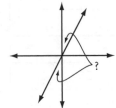

f.
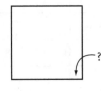

g.
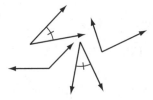

h.
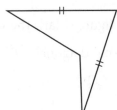

i. $m\angle A = 87°$
$m\angle X = 96°$
$m\angle Y = 90°$

j.
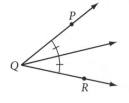

k.
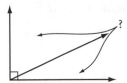

l.
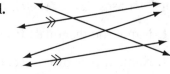

1. _____ Pair of vertical angles

2. _____ Pair of supplementary angles

3. _____ Right angle

4. _____ Obtuse angle

5. _____ Pair of congruent angles

6. _____ Pair of complementary angles

7. _____ Linear pair of angles

8. _____ Acute angle

9. _____ Bisected angle

10. _____ Parallel lines

11. _____ Congruent segments

12. _____ Perpendicular lines

13. Give two examples of parallel lines in real-world situations.

14. If $m\angle P = 13°$, $m\angle Q = 77°$, and $\angle Q$ and $\angle R$ are complementary, what can you conclude about $\angle P$ and $\angle R$? Explain your reasoning.

For Exercises 15–17, sketch, label, and mark a figure showing each property.

15. $\ell_1 \parallel \ell_2, \ell_2 \perp \ell_3$ **16.** $\overline{PQ} \perp \overrightarrow{PR}$ **17.** $\angle BAC \cong \angle XAY, CX = BC$

Lesson 1.4 • Polygons

Name _____ Period _____ Date _____

For Exercises 1–8, complete the table.

Polygon name	Number of sides	Number of diagonals
1. Triangle		
2.		2
3.	5	
4. Hexagon		
5. Heptagon		
6.	8	
7.		35
8.	12	

For Exercises 9–11, sketch and label each figure. Mark the congruences.

9. Concave pentagon *PENTA*, with external diagonal $\overline{ET}$, and $\overline{TA} \cong \overline{PE}$.

10. Equilateral quadrilateral *QUAD*, with $\angle Q \not\cong \angle U$.

11. Regular octagon *ABCDEFGH*.

For Exercises 12–15, sketch and use hexagon *ABCDEF*.

12. Name the diagonals from *A*.

13. Name a pair of consecutive sides.

14. Name a pair of consecutive angles.

15. Name a pair of non-intersecting diagonals.

For Exercises 16–19, use these figures at right.

MNOPQ ≅ *RSTUV*

16. $m\angle N =$ _____

17. $VR =$ _____

18. $m\angle P =$ _____

19. $ON =$ _____

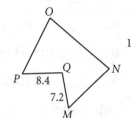
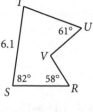

20. How many different (noncongruent) convex quadrilaterals can you make on a 3-by-3 dot grid, using the dots as vertices?

Lesson 1.5 • Triangles and Special Quadrilaterals

Name _____ Period _____ Date _____

For Exercises 1–7, use the figure at right. Name a pair of

1. Parallel segments
2. Perpendicular segments
3. Congruent segments
4. Complementary angles
5. Supplementary angles
6. Linear angles
7. Vertical angles

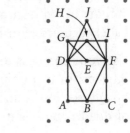

For Exercises 8–12, sketch, label, and mark each figure.

8. Isosceles obtuse triangle *TRI* with vertex angle *T*.

9. Rhombus *RHOM* with acute ∠*H* and the shorter diagonal.

10. Scalene right triangle *SCA* with midpoints *L*, *M*, and *N* on $\overline{SC}$, $\overline{CA}$, and $\overline{SA}$, respectively.

11. Trapezoid *TRAP* with $\overline{TR} \parallel \overline{AP}$, $\overline{RE} \perp \overline{PA}$, and *P*, *E*, and *A* collinear.

12. Kite *KITE* with *EK* = *KI* and obtuse ∠*K*.

For Exercises 13–22, name each polygon in the figure. Assume that the grid is square.

13. Square	14. Rectangle
15. Parallelogram	16. Trapezoid
17. Rhombus	18. Kite
19. Concave quadrilateral	20. Isosceles triangle
21. Scalene triangle	22. Right triangle

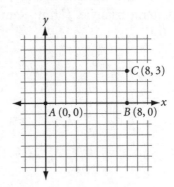

For Exercises 23–26, use the graph at right.

23. Locate *D* so that *ABCD* is a rectangle.

24. Locate *E* so that *ABCE* is a trapezoid.

25. Locate *F* so that *ABF* is a right triangle.

26. Locate *G* so that *A*, *B*, *C*, and *G* determine a parallelogram that is not a rectangle.

Lesson 1.6 • Circles

Name _____ Period _____ Date _____

1. Use a compass, protractor, and straightedge to draw circle *O* with diameter $\overline{AB}$; radius $\overline{OC}$ with $\overline{OC} \perp \overline{AB}$; $\overline{OD}$, the angle bisector of $\angle AOC$, with *D* on the circle; chords $\overline{AC}$ and $\overline{BC}$; and a tangent at *D*.

For Exercises 2–5, use the figure at right.

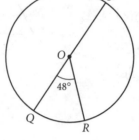

2. $m\widehat{QR} =$ _____   3. $m\widehat{PR} =$ _____

4. $m\widehat{PQR} =$ _____   5. $m\widehat{QPR} =$ _____

For Exercises 6–8, give the measure of the central angle formed by the hands of a clock at each time.

6. 1:00

7. 2:30

8. 6:45

9. Use a compass to construct a circle. Label the center *P*. Sketch two parallel tangents. Connect the points of tangency. What do you notice about the chord?

10. Sketch a circle with an inscribed pentagon.

11. Sketch a circle with a circumscribed quadrilateral.

12. A circle with center at (3, 2) goes through the point (−2, 2). Give the coordinates of three other points on the circle.

13. Use your compass and protractor to make an arc with measure 50°, an arc with measure 180°, and an arc with measure 290°. Label each arc with its measure.

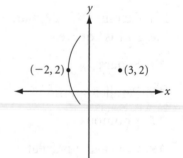

14. Use your compass to construct two circles with different radii that intersect in two points. Label the centers *P* and *Q* and the points of intersection *A* and *B*. Construct quadrilateral *PAQB*. What type of quadrilateral is it?

15. Use your compass and straightedge to construct a circle with an inscribed equilateral triangle. (Hint: Remember the daisy designs from Chapter 0.)

Discovering Geometry Practice Your Skills
©2003 Key Curriculum Press

Lesson 1.7 • A Picture Is Worth a Thousand Words

Name _____ Period _____ Date _____

Read and reread each problem carefully, determining what information you are given and what it is that you trying to find.

1. A pair of parallel interstate gas and power lines run 10 meters apart and are equally distant from relay station *A*. The power company needs to locate a gas-monitoring point on one of the lines exactly 12 meters from relay station *A*. Draw a diagram showing the locus of possible locations.

2. Motion-efficiency expert Martha G. Rigsby needs to locate a supply point equally distant from two major work-inspection stations in an electronics assembly plant. The workstations are 30 meters apart and are each positioned halfway between a pair of parallel heat-sensitive walls. The walls are 24 meters apart. The supply point must be at least 4, and at most 20, meters from either wall. Draw a diagram of the locus of possible locations.

3. The six members of the Senica High School 10th-grade math club are to have a group photo taken for the yearbook. The photographer has asked each group to submit the height of each member so that he can quickly arrange them in order. The math club sent him the following information. Anica is 4 inches taller than Bruce. Charles is the same height as Ellen but an inch taller than Anica. Fred is midway between Bruce and Dora. Dora is 2 inches taller than Anica. Help out the photographer and arrange the club members in order from tallest to shortest.

4. Sketch a possible net for each solid.

a.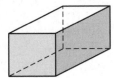

b.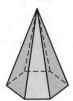

c.

Lesson 1.8 • Space Geometry

Name _____ **Period** _____ **Date** _____

For Exercises 1–3, draw each figure.

1. A prism with a rectangular base.

2. A cylinder with base diameter greater than height.

3. A cone on a sphere, like a hat on a head.

For Exercises 4 and 5, sketch the three-dimensional figure formed by folding each net into a solid. Name the solid.

4.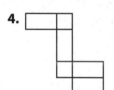

5.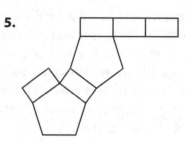

For Exercises 6 and 7, sketch the section formed when each solid is sliced by the plane as shown.

6.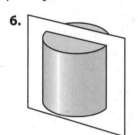

7.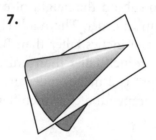

For Exercises 8 and 9, sketch a 2-by-3-by-4 rectangular prism showing the 1-by-1 building cubes.

8. Sketch the prism looking straight at a vertical edge from a point slightly above the prism.

9. Sketch the prism looking straight at a face from a point slightly to the right and slightly above the prism.

10. The prism below is built with 1-cm cubes. How many cubes are completely hidden from sight?

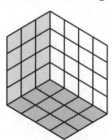

11. Find the lengths of x and y.

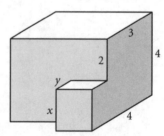

Discovering Geometry Practice Your Skills
©2003 Key Curriculum Press

Lesson 2.1 • Inductive Reasoning

Name _____ Period _____ Date _____

For Exercises 1–8, use inductive reasoning to find the next two terms in each sequence.

1. 4, 8, 12, 16, _____, _____

2. 400, 200, 100, 50, 25, _____, _____

3. $\frac{1}{8}, \frac{2}{7}, \frac{1}{2}, \frac{4}{5},$ _____, _____

4. −5, 3, −2, 1, −1, 0, _____, _____

5. 360, 180, 120, 90, _____, _____

6. 1, 3, 9, 27, 81, _____, _____

7. 1, 5, 17, 53, 161, _____, _____

8. 1, 5, 14, 30, 55, _____, _____

For Exercises 9–12, use inductive reasoning to draw the next two shapes in each picture pattern.

9. **10.**

11.

12.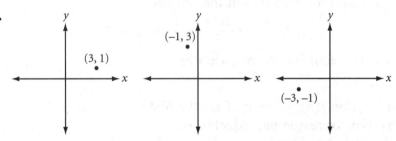

For Exercises 13–15, use inductive reasoning to test each conjecture. Decide if the conjecture seems true or false. If it seems false, give a counterexample.

13. Every odd whole number can be written as the difference of two squares.

14. Every whole number greater than 1 can be written as the sum of two prime numbers.

15. The square of a number is larger than the number.

Lesson 2.2 • Deductive Reasoning

Name _____ Period _____ Date _____

1. $\triangle ABC$ is equilateral. Is $\triangle ABD$ equilateral? What type of reasoning, inductive or deductive, do you use when solving this problem?

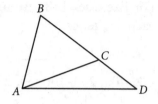

2. If 6 # 8 = 7, 10 # 3 = $6\frac{1}{2}$, and -3 # $-2 = -2.5$, then

   4 # 8 = _____ -5 # 0 = _____   2 # 2 = _____

   What type of reasoning, inductive or deductive, do you use when solving this problem?

3. $\angle A$ and $\angle D$ are complementary. $\angle A$ and $\angle E$ are supplementary. What can you conclude about $\angle D$ and $\angle E$? What type of reasoning, inductive or deductive, do you use when solving this problem?

4.

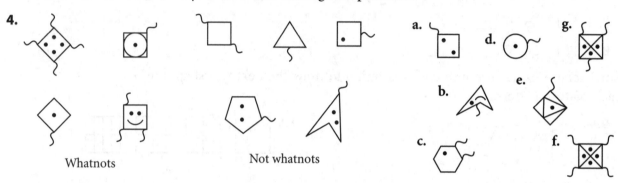

Whatnots

Not whatnots

Which are whatnots?

What type of reasoning, inductive or deductive, do you use when solving this problem?

5. Solve each equation for x. Give a reason for each step in the process.

   a. $4x + 3(2 - x) = 8 - 2x$ b. $\dfrac{19 - 2(3x - 1)}{5} = x + 2$

   What type of reasoning, inductive or deductive, do you use when solving these problems?

6. A sequence is generated by the function $f(n) = 5 - n^2$. Give the first five terms in the sequence. What type of reasoning, inductive or deductive, do you use when solving this problem?

7. A sequence begins $-4, 1, 6, 11 \ldots$

   a. Give the next two terms in the sequence. What type of reasoning, inductive or deductive, do you use when solving this problem?

   b. Find a rule that generates the sequence. Then give the 50th term in the sequence. What type of reasoning, inductive or deductive, do you use when solving this problem?

8. Choose any 3-digit number. Multiply it by 7. Multiply the result by 11. Then multiply the result by 13. Do you notice anything? Try a few other 3-digit numbers and make a conjecture. Use deductive reasoning to explain why your conjecture is true.

Lesson 2.3 • Finding the *n*th Term

Name _____ Period _____ Date _____

For Exercises 1–4, tell whether or not the rule is a linear function.

1.

n	1	2	3	4	5
f(n)	8	15	22	29	36

2.

n	1	2	3	4	5
g(n)	14	11	8	5	2

3.

n	1	2	3	4	5
h(n)	−9	−6	−2	3	9

4.

n	1	2	3	4	5
j(n)	$-\frac{3}{2}$	−1	$-\frac{1}{2}$	0	$\frac{1}{2}$

For Exercises 5 and 6, complete each table.

5.

n		1	2	3	4	5	6
f(n) = 7n − 12							

6.

n		1	2	3	4	5	6
g(n) = −8n − 2							

For Exercises 7–9, find the function rule for each sequence. Then find the 50th term in the sequence.

7.

n	1	2	3	4	5	6	. . .	n	. . .	50
f(n)	9	13	17	21	25	29				

8.

n	1	2	3	4	5	6	. . .	n	. . .	50
g(n)	6	1	−4	−9	−14	−19				

9.

n	1	2	3	4	5	6	. . .	n	. . .	50
h(n)	6.5	7	7.5	8	8.5	9				

10. Find the rule for the number of tiles in the *n*th figure. Then find the number of tiles in the 200th figure.

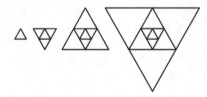

n	1	2	3	4	5	. . .	n	. . .	200
Number of tiles	1	4	7						

11. Sketch the next figure in the sequence. Then complete the table.

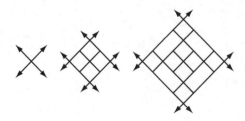

n	1	2	3	4	. . .	n	. . .	50
Number of segments and lines	2	6						
Number of regions of the plane	4							

Lesson 2.4 • Mathematical Modeling

Name _____ **Period** _____ **Date** _____

1. If you toss a coin, you will get a head or a tail. Copy and complete the geometric model to show all possible results of four consecutive tosses.

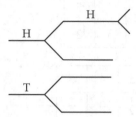

   How many sequences of results are possible? How many sequences have exactly one tail? Assuming a head or a tail is equally likely, what is the probability of getting exactly one head in four tosses?

2. If there are 12 people sitting around a table, how many different pairs of people can have conversations during dinner, assuming they can all talk to each other? What geometric figure can you use to model this situation?

3. Tournament games and results are often displayed using a geometric model. Two examples are shown below. Sketch a geometric model for a tournament involving 4 teams and a tournament involving 6 teams. Each team must have the same chance to win. Try to have as few games as possible in each tournament. Show the total number of games in each tournament. Name the teams a, b, c . . . and number the games 1, 2, 3 . . . .

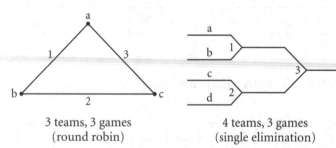

3 teams, 3 games   4 teams, 3 games
(round robin)   (single elimination)

Discovering Geometry Practice Your Skills
©2003 Key Curriculum Press

Lesson 2.5 • Angle Relationships

Name _____ Period _____ Date _____

For Exercises 1–8, find each lettered angle measure without using a protractor.

1.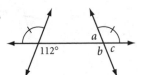

2.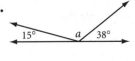

3.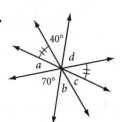

4.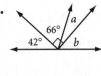

5.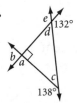

6.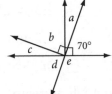

7.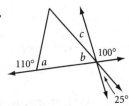

8.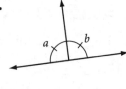

For Exercises 9–14, tell whether each statement is always (A), sometimes (S), or never (N) true.

9. _____ The sum of the measures of two acute angles equals the measure of an obtuse angle.

10. _____ If ∠*XAY* and ∠*PAQ* are vertical angles, then either *X*, *A*, and *P* or *X*, *A*, and *Q* are collinear.

11. _____ The sum of the measures of two obtuse angles equals the measure of an obtuse angle.

12. _____ The difference between the measures of the supplement and the complement of an angle is 90°.

13. _____ If two angles form a linear pair, then they are complementary.

14. _____ If a statement is true, then its converse is true.

For Exercises 15–19, fill in each blank to make a true statement.

15. If one angle of a linear pair is obtuse, then the other is _____.

16. If ∠*A* ≅ ∠*B* and the supplement of ∠*B* has measure 22°, then
$m∠A =$ _____.

17. If ∠*P* is a right angle and ∠*P* and ∠*Q* form a linear pair, then
$m∠Q$ is _____.

18. If ∠*S* and ∠*T* are complementary and ∠*T* and ∠*U* are supplementary, then ∠*U* is a(n) _____ angle.

19. Switching the "if" and "then" parts of a statement changes the statement to its _____.

Lesson 2.6 • Special Angles on Parallel Lines

Name _____ Period _____ Date _____

For Exercises 1–11, use the figure at right.

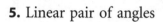

For Exercises 1–5, find an example of each term.

1. Corresponding angles   **2.** Alternate interior angles

3. Alternate exterior angles   **4.** Vertical angles

5. Linear pair of angles

For Exercises 6–11, tell whether each statement is always (A), sometimes (S), or never (N) true.

6. _____ ∠1 ≅ ∠3   **7.** _____ ∠3 ≅ ∠8

8. _____ ∠2 and ∠6 are supplementary.   **9.** _____ ∠7 and ∠8 are supplementary.

10. _____ $m\angle 1 \neq m\angle 6$ **11.** _____ $m\angle 5 = m\angle 4$

For Exercises 12–14, use your conjectures to find each angle measure.

12.

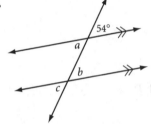

13.

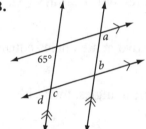

14.

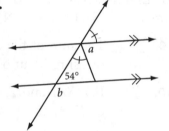

For Exercises 15–17, use your conjectures to determine whether or not $\ell_1 \parallel \ell_2$, and explain why. If not enough information is given, write "cannot be determined."

15.

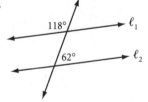

16.

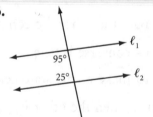

17.

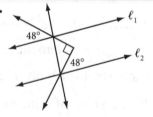

18. Find each angle measure.

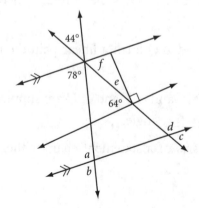

Lesson 3.1 • Duplicating Segments and Angles

Name _____ Period _____ Date _____

In Exercises 1–3, use the segments and angles below.

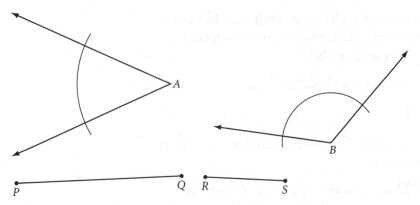

1. Using only a compass and straightedge, duplicate each segment and angle. There is an arc in each angle to help you.

2. Construct a line segment with length $3PQ - 2RS$.

3. Duplicate the two angles so that the angles have the same vertex and share a common side and the nonshared side of one angle falls inside the other angle. Then use a protractor to measure the three angles you created. Write an equation relating their measures.

4. Use a compass and straightedge to construct an isosceles triangle with two sides congruent to $\overline{AB}$ and base congruent to $\overline{CD}$.

A ————————————————•B C•————•D

5. Repeat Exercise 4 with patty paper and a straightedge.

6. Construct an equilateral triangle with sides congruent to $\overline{CD}$.

C•————————————•D

7. Draw an acute angle and a segment on the top half of your paper. On the bottom half, construct an isosceles triangle using the angle and segment. How many different (noncongruent) isosceles triangles could you construct with those parts?

Lesson 3.2 • Constructing Perpendicular Bisectors

Name _____ Period _____ Date _____

1. Draw a segment and construct its perpendicular bisector.

2. Construct two congruent segments that are the perpendicular bisectors of each other. Form a quadrilateral by connecting the four endpoints. What type of quadrilateral does this seem to be?

3. Duplicate $\overline{AB}$. Then construct a segment with length $\frac{5}{4}AB$.

A •————————————————————• B

4. In $\triangle ABC$ with $A(0, 0)$, $B(9, 0)$, and $C(6, 12)$, find the midpoint of each side and the slope of each midsegment.

5. Draw a segment; label it $\overline{CM}$. $\overline{CM}$ is a median of $\triangle ABC$. Construct $\triangle ABC$. Is $\triangle ABC$ unique? If not, construct a different triangle, $\triangle A'B'C$, also having $\overline{CM}$ as a median.

6. Draw a segment; label it $\overline{PQ}$. $\overline{PQ}$ is a midsegment of $\triangle ABC$. Construct $\triangle ABC$. Is $\triangle ABC$ unique? If not, construct a different triangle, $\triangle A'B'C'$, also having $\overline{PQ}$ as a midsegment.

7. Construct a right triangle. Label it $\triangle ABC$ with right angle B. Construct median $\overline{BD}$. Compare BD, AD, and CD.

8. Complete each statement as fully as possible.

    a. L is equidistant from _____.

    b. M is equidistant from _____.

    c. N is equidistant from _____.

    d. O is equidistant from _____.

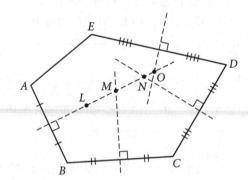

Discovering Geometry Practice Your Skills
©2003 Key Curriculum Press

Lesson 3.3 • Constructing Perpendiculars to a Line

Name _____ Period _____ Date _____

For Exercises 1–5, decide whether each statement is true or false. If the statement is false, explain why or give a counterexample.

1. In a triangle, an altitude is shorter than either side from the same vertex.

2. In a triangle, an altitude is shorter than the median from the same vertex.

3. In a triangle, if a perpendicular bisector of a side and an altitude coincide, then the triangle is isosceles.

4. Exactly one altitude lies outside a triangle.

5. The intersection of the perpendicular bisectors of the sides lies inside the triangle.

6. Construct a rectangle with sides equal in length to $\overline{AB}$ and $\overline{CD}$.

```
•————————————————————•  •—————————•
A                    B  C         D
```

7. Mark two points, P and Q, on patty paper. Fold the paper to construct square PQRS.

8. Construct a large equilateral triangle. Let P be any point inside the triangle. Construct $\overline{WX}$ equal in length to the sum of the distances from P to each of the sides. Let Q be any other point inside the triangle. Construct $\overline{YZ}$ equal in length to the sum of the distances from Q to each side. Compare WX and YZ.

Lesson 3.4 • Constructing Angle Bisectors

Name _____ Period _____ Date _____

1. Draw an obtuse angle. Use a compass and straightedge to construct the angle bisector. Draw another obtuse angle and fold to construct the angle bisector.

2. Draw a large triangle on patty paper. Fold to construct the three angle bisectors. What do you notice?

3. Complete each statement as fully as possible.

   a. *M* is equidistant from _____.

   b. *P* is equidistant from _____.

   c. *Q* is equidistant from _____.

   d. *R* is equidistant from _____.

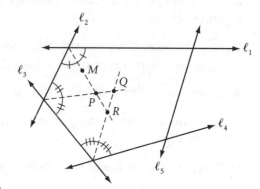

4. If the converse of the Angle Bisector Conjecture is true, what can you conclude about this figure?

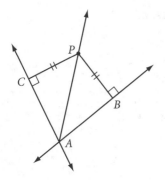

5. Construct right triangle *RGH* with right angle *R*. Construct median $\overline{RM}$, perpendicular $\overline{MN}$ from *M* to $\overline{RG}$, and perpendicular $\overline{MO}$ from *M* to $\overline{RH}$. Compare *RN* and *GN*, and compare *RO* and *HO*.

6. Draw obtuse △*ABC* with acute ∠*A*. From ∠*A* construct median $\overline{AD}$, altitude $\overline{AE}$, and angle bisector $\overline{AF}$ with *F* on $\overline{BC}$. Order the distances *AB*, *AC*, *AD*, *AE*, and *AF* in two possible ways.

   _____ > _____ > _____ > _____ > _____

   or

   _____ > _____ > _____ > _____ > _____

Discovering Geometry Practice Your Skills
©2003 Key Curriculum Press

Lesson 3.5 • Constructing Parallel Lines

Name _____ Period _____ Date _____

1. Draw a line and a point not on the line. Use a compass and straightedge to construct a line through the given point parallel to the given line.

2. Repeat Exercise 1 but draw the line and point on patty paper and fold to construct the parallel line.

3. Use a compass and straightedge to construct a parallelogram.

4. Use patty paper and a straightedge to construct an isosceles trapezoid.

5. Construct a rhombus with sides equal in length to $\overline{AB}$ and having an angle congruent to $\angle P$.

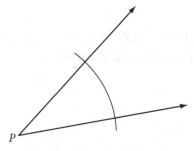

6. Construct trapezoid *ZOID* with $\overline{ZO}$ and $\overline{ID}$ as nonparallel sides and *AB* as the distance between the parallel sides.

Z _____ O I _____ D A _____ B

In Exercises 7–15, use the figure to determine whether each statement is true, false, or cannot be determined.

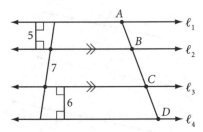

7. $AB < BC$	**8.** $AB < CD$
9. $6 \leq CD$	**10.** The distance between ℓ_2 and ℓ_3 is 7.
11. $BD > AC$	**12.** $AB > 5$
13. $CD > 5$	**14.** The distance between ℓ_1 and ℓ_4 is at least 18.

15. The distance between ℓ_1 and ℓ_4 is at most 18.

Lesson 3.6 • Construction Problems

Name _____ **Period** _____ **Date** _____

1. Construct kite *KITE* using these parts.
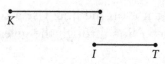
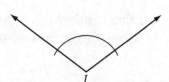

2. Construct a rectangle with perimeter the length of this segment.

3. Use a compass and straightedge to construct a rectangle with this
segment as its diagonal. Then repeat the construction with patty
paper and a straightedge.

4. Draw obtuse △*OBT*. Construct and label the three altitudes $\overline{OU}$, $\overline{BS}$,
and $\overline{TE}$.

5. Construct a triangle congruent to △*ABC*. Describe your steps. Then
construct another congruent triangle a different way.

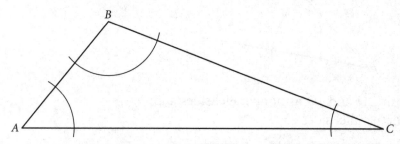

In Exercises 6–8, construct a triangle using the given parts. Then, if
possible, construct a different (noncongruent) triangle using the
same parts.

6.

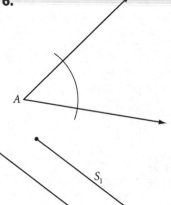

7.

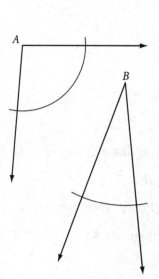

8.

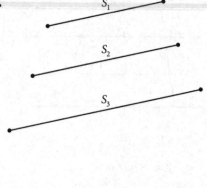

Discovering Geometry Practice Your Skills
©2003 Key Curriculum Press

Lesson 3.7 • Constructing Points of Concurrency

Name _____ **Period** _____ **Date** _____

1. A circular revolving sprinkler needs to be set up to water every part of a triangular garden. Where should the sprinkler be located so that it reaches all of the garden, but doesn't spray farther than necessary?

2. You need to supply electric power to three transformers, one on each of three roads enclosing a large triangular track of land. Each transformer should be the same distance from the power-generation plant and as close to the plant as possible. Where should you build the power plant, and where should you locate each transformer?

3. Draw an obtuse triangle. Construct the inscribed and the circumscribed circles.

4. Construct an equilateral triangle. Construct the inscribed and the circumscribed circles. How does this construction differ from Exercise 3?

5. Construct a square. Construct the inscribed and circumscribed circles.

6. Construct two obtuse, two acute, and two right triangles. Locate the circumcenter of each triangle. Make a conjecture about the relationship between the location of the circumcenter and the measure of the angles.

Lesson 3.8 • The Centroid

Name _____ **Period** _____ **Date** _____

1. Draw a large acute triangle. Construct the centroid.

2. Construct a regular hexagon and locate its center of gravity.

3. Use a ruler and compass to find the center of gravity of a sheet-metal triangle with sides measuring 6 cm, 8 cm, and 10 cm. How far is the center from each vertex, to the nearest tenth of a centimeter?

4. $\triangle ABC$ has vertices $A(9, 12)$, $B(-3, 2)$, and $C(3, -2)$. Find the centroid.

5. $PL = 24$, $QC = 10$, and $KC = 7$. Find PC, CL, QM, and CR.

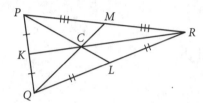

6. Identify each statement as describing the incenter, circumcenter, orthocenter, or centroid.

   a. _____ The point equally distant from the three sides of a triangle.

   b. _____ The center of gravity of a thin metal triangle.

   c. _____ The point equidistant from the three vertices.

   d. _____ The intersection of the perpendicular bisectors of the sides of a triangle.

   e. _____ The intersection of the altitudes of a triangle.

   f. _____ The intersection of the angle bisectors of a triangle.

   g. _____ The intersection of the medians of a triangle.

   h. _____ A point always inside the triangle and on the Euler line.

   i. _____ The point on the hypotenuse of a right triangle.

   j. _____ The point at a vertex of a right triangle.

Discovering Geometry Practice Your Skills
©2003 Key Curriculum Press

Lesson 4.1 • Triangle Sum Conjecture

Name _____ Period _____ Date _____

In Exercises 1–9, determine the angle measures.

1. $p =$ _____, $q =$ _____

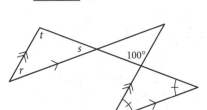

2. $x =$ _____, $y =$ _____

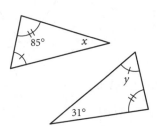

3. $a =$ _____, $b =$ _____

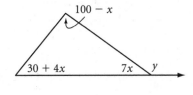

4. $r =$ _____, $s =$ _____,

  $t =$ _____

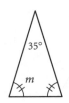

5. $x =$ _____, $y =$ _____

6. $y =$ _____

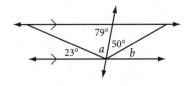

7. $s =$ _____

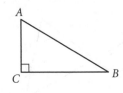

8. $m =$ _____

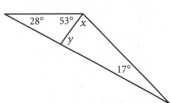

9. $m\angle P =$ _____

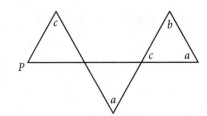

10. Explain why $\angle A$ and $\angle B$ are complementary.

A
C B

11. Find the sum of the measures of the marked angles.

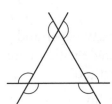

12. Explain why $m\angle A + m\angle B = m\angle C + m\angle D$.

B D
  E
A   C

13. Find the measure of $\angle QPT$.

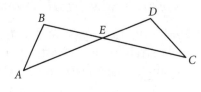

14. In isosceles $\triangle ABC$ the measure of vertex $\angle ABC$ is 80°. If D is the incenter of the triangle, what is the measure of $\angle ADB$?

Lesson 4.2 • Properties of Special Triangles

Name _____ Period _____ Date _____

In Exercises 1–3, find the angle measures.

1. $m\angle T =$ _____

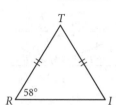

2. $m\angle G =$ _____

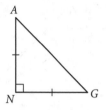

3. $x =$ _____

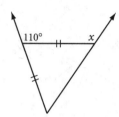

4. a. Name the angle(s) congruent to $\angle A$.

b. Name the segment(s) congruent to $\overline{BC}$.

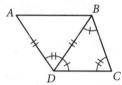

5. a. Name the angle(s) congruent to $\angle DAB$.

b. Name the angle(s) congruent to $\angle ADB$.

c. What can you conclude about $\overline{AD}$ and $\overline{BC}$? Why?

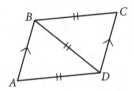

6. Explain why $\triangle PQR$ is isosceles.

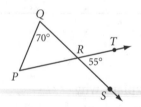

7. $x =$ _____ , $y =$ _____

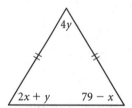

8. $PR = QR$ and $QS = RS$. If $m\angle RSQ = 120°$, what is $m\angle QPR$?

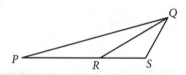

9. Name all angles congruent to $\angle CGI$ in the figure at right. Explain why $\triangle JBH$ is isosceles.

10. Using a compass and a straightedge or patty paper and a straightedge, construct an isosceles triangle with a base angle that measures 75°. Explain your method.

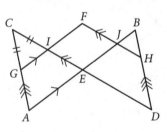

In Exercises 11 and 12, find the missing coordinates.

11.

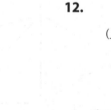

12.

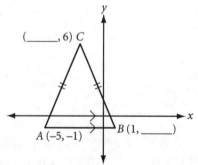

Lesson 4.3 • Triangle Inequalities

Name _____ Period _____ Date _____

In Exercises 1–4, determine whether it is possible to draw a triangle with sides of the given measures. If it is possible, write yes. If it is not possible, write no and make a sketch demonstrating why it is not possible.

1. 16 cm, 30 cm, 45 cm

2. 9 km, 17 km, 28 km

3. 32 in., 60 in., 87 in.

4. 13.4 ft, 17.7 ft, 31.1 ft

In Exercises 5 and 6, use a compass and straightedge to construct a triangle with the given sides. If it is not possible, explain why not.

5.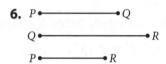

6.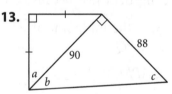

7. If 17 and 36 are the lengths of two sides of a triangle, what is the range of possible values for the length of the third side?

In Exercises 8–13, arrange the unknown measures in order from greatest to least.

8.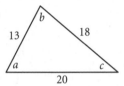

9.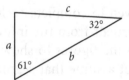

10.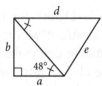

11.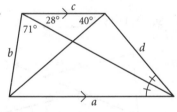

12.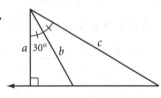

13.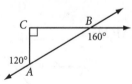

14. x = _____

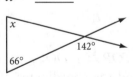

15. x = _____

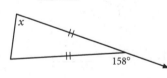

16. What's wrong with this picture?

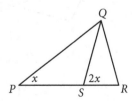

17. Explain why △PQS is isosceles.

18. Explain why the sum of the three altitudes of a triangle is always less than its perimeter.

Lesson 4.4 • Are There Congruence Shortcuts?

Name _____ Period _____ Date _____

In Exercises 1–3, use a compass and a straightedge or patty paper and a straightedge to construct a triangle with the given parts. Then, if possible, construct a different (noncongruent) triangle with the same parts. If it is not possible, explain why not.

1.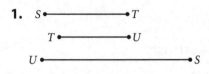

2.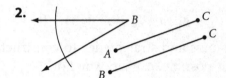

3.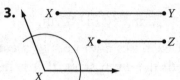

In Exercises 4–6, name the conjecture that leads to each congruence.

4. △*PAT* ≅ △*IMT*

5. △*SID* ≅ △*JAN*

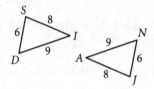

6. $\overline{TS}$ bisects $\overline{MA}$, $\overline{MT} \cong \overline{AT}$, and △*MST* ≅ △*AST*

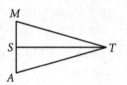

In Exercises 7–11, use the information given to complete each statement. If the triangles cannot be shown to be congruent from the information given, write "cannot be determined" and redraw the figures to show that the triangles are clearly not congruent. Do not assume that segments or angles are congruent just because they appear to be congruent.

7. *M* is the midpoint of $\overline{AB}$ and $\overline{PQ}$.

△*APM* ≅ △ _____

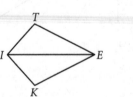

8. *KITE* is a kite with *KI* = *TI*.

△*KIE* ≅ △ _____

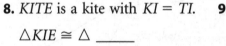

9. △*ABC* ≅ _____

10. △*MON* ≅ _____

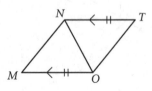

11. △*SQR* = _____

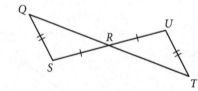

12. △*TOP* ≅ △*DOG*. Find the coordinates of *D* and *G*.

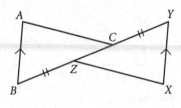

Discovering Geometry Practice Your Skills
©2003 Key Curriculum Press

Lesson 4.5 • Are There Other Congruence Shortcuts?

Name _____ **Period** _____ **Date** _____

1. Use a compass and a straightedge or patty paper and a straightedge to construct △*PQR* from the given parts. How does your triangle compare to the triangle constructed by others in your class? Explain.

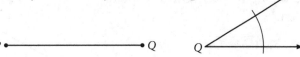

2. Use a compass and a straightedge or patty paper and a straightedge to construct △*ABC*. Explain your procedure. What conjecture tells you that your triangle is congruent to the triangle of another student?

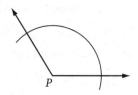
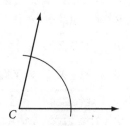

In Exercises 3–8, use the information given to complete each statement. If the triangles cannot be shown to be congruent from the information given, write "cannot be determined" and redraw the figures to show that the triangles are clearly not congruent. Do not assume that segments or angles are congruent just because they appear to be congruent.

3. △*PIT* ≅ △ _____

4. △*XVW* ≅ △ _____

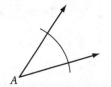

5. △*ECD* ≅ △ _____

6. $\overline{PS}$ is the angle bisector of ∠*QPR*.

 △*PQS* ≅ △ _____

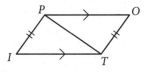

7. △*ACN* ≅ △ _____

8. *EFGH* is a parallelogram. *GQ = EQ*.

 △*EQL* ≅ △ _____

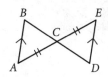

9. Name three pairs of congruent triangles. For each pair, explain how you know they are congruent.

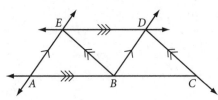

10. △*ABC* ≅ △*PQR*. Find the coordinates of *Q* and *R*. Show that $\overline{BC} \parallel \overline{QR}$.

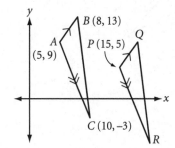

Lesson 4.6 • Corresponding Parts of Congruent Triangles

Name _____ Period _____ Date _____

1. Give the shorthand name for each of the four triangle congruence conjectures.

In Exercises 2 and 3, use the figures at right to explain why each congruence is true.

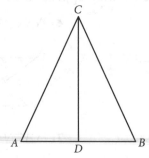

2. $\angle A \cong \angle P$ **3.** $\overline{BC} \cong \overline{QR}$

In Exercises 4–7, use the figure at right to explain why each congruence is true. *WXYZ* is a parallelogram.

4. $\angle WXZ \cong \angle YZX$ **5.** $\angle WZX \cong \angle YXZ$

6. $\triangle WZX \cong \triangle YXZ$ **7.** $\angle W \cong \angle Y$

For Exercises 8 and 9, copy the figures onto your paper and mark them with the given information. To demonstrate whether or not the segments or the angles indicated are congruent, determine that two triangles are congruent. Then, state which conjecture proves them congruent.

8. *M* is the midpoint of $\overline{WX}$ and $\overline{YZ}$. Is $\overline{YW} \cong \overline{ZX}$? Why?

9. $\triangle ABC$ is isosceles and $\overline{CD}$ is the bisector of the vertex angle. Is $\overline{AD} \cong \overline{BD}$? Why?

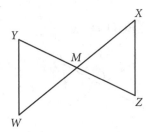

In Exercises 10 and 11, use the figure at right to write a paragraph proof for each statement.

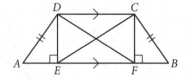

10. $\overline{DE} \cong \overline{CF}$ **11.** $\overline{EC} \cong \overline{FD}$

12. *TRAP* is an isosceles trapezoid with $TP = RA$ and $\angle PTR \cong \angle ART$. Write a paragraph proof explaining why $\overline{TA} \cong \overline{RP}$.

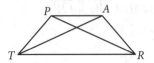

Discovering Geometry Practice Your Skills
©2003 Key Curriculum Press

Lesson 4.7 • Flowchart Thinking

Name _____ Period _____ Date _____

Complete or write a flowchart for each proof.

1. Given: $\overline{PQ} \parallel \overline{SR}$ and $\overline{PQ} \cong \overline{SR}$

   Show: $\overline{SP} \cong \overline{QR}$

Flowchart Proof

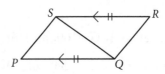

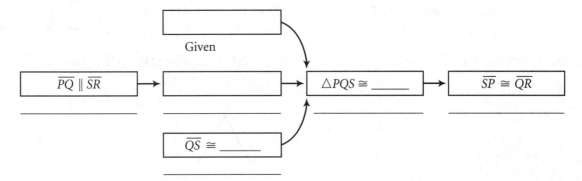

2. Given: Kite $KITE$ with $\overline{KE} \cong \overline{KI}$

   Show: $\overline{KT}$ bisects $\angle EKI$ and $\angle ETI$

Flowchart Proof

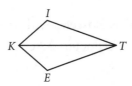

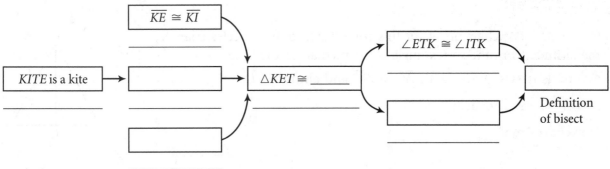

3. Given: $ABCD$ is a parallelogram

   Show: $\angle A \cong \angle C$

Flowchart Proof

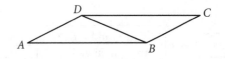

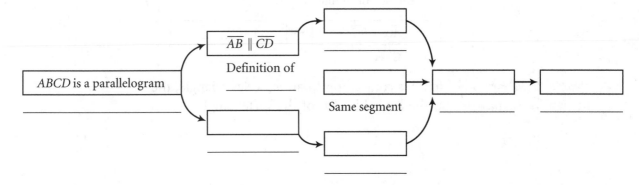

Lesson 4.8 • Proving Isosceles Triangle Conjectures

Name _____ Period _____ Date _____

In Exercises 1–3, use the figure at right. $\triangle ABC$ is isosceles
with $AC = BC$.

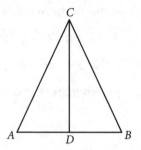

1. $\overline{CD}$ is a median, perimeter $\triangle ABC = 60$, and $AC = 22$. $AD =$ _____

2. $\overline{CD}$ is an angle bisector, and $m\angle A = 54°$. $m\angle ACD =$ _____

3. $\overline{CD}$ is an altitude, perimeter $\triangle ABC = 55$, $m\angle ACD = 19°$, and $AD = 8$.
   $m\angle B =$ _____, $CB =$ _____

4. $\triangle EQU$ is equilateral.

   $m\angle E =$ _____

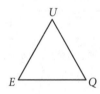

5. $\triangle ANG$ is equiangular and perimeter
   $\triangle ANG = 51$. $AN =$ _____

6. $\triangle ABC$ is equilateral, $\triangle ACD$ is isosceles with base $\overline{AC}$,
   perimeter $\triangle ABC = 66$, and perimeter $\triangle ACD = 82$.
   Perimeter $ABCD =$ _____

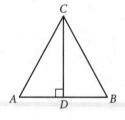

7. Complete a flowchart proof for this conjecture: In an isosceles triangle,
   the altitude from the vertex angle is the median to the base.

   Given: Isosceles $\triangle ABC$ with $\overline{AC} \cong \overline{BC}$ and altitude $\overline{CD}$

   Show: $\overline{CD}$ is a median

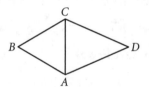

Flowchart Proof

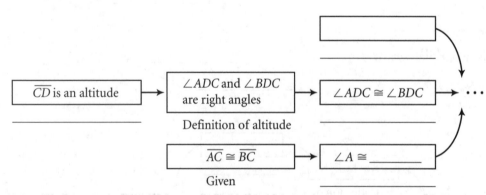

8. Write a flowchart proof for this conjecture: In an isosceles triangle, the
   median to the base is also the angle bisector of the vertex angle.

Lesson 5.1 • Polygon Sum Conjecture

Name _____ Period _____ Date _____

In Exercises 1–4, find each lettered angle measure.

1.

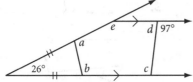

2.

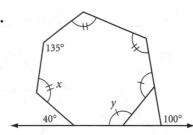

3.

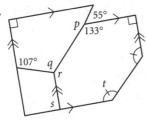

4.

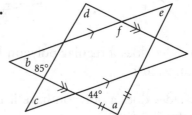

5. Use a protractor to draw pentagon *ABCDE* with *m∠A* = 85°, *m∠B* = 125°, *m∠C* = 110°, and *m∠D* = 70°. What is *m∠E*? Measure it, and check your work by calculating.

6. One exterior angle of a regular polygon measures 10°. What is the measure of each interior angle? How many sides does the polygon have?

7. The sum of the measures of the interior angles of a regular polygon is 2340°. How many sides does the polygon have?

8. *ABCD* is a square. *ABE* is an equilateral triangle.

x = _____

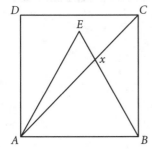

9. *ABCDEF* is a regular hexagon. *ABGH* is a square.

x = _____

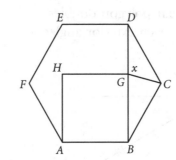

10. *ABCDE* is a regular pentagon. *ABFG* is a square.

x = _____

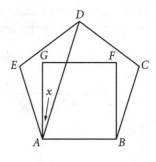

11. Find *m∠HFD*.

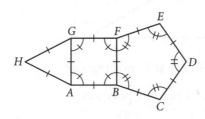

Lesson 5.2 • Exterior Angles of a Polygon

Name _____ Period _____ Date _____

In Exercises 1–3, find each lettered angle measure.

1. $a = $ _____, $b = $ _____

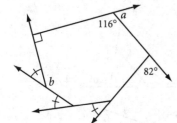

2. $a = $ _____, $b = $ _____

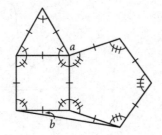

3. $a = $ _____, $b = $ _____, $c = $ _____

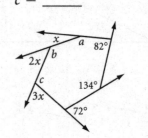

4. How many sides does a regular polygon have if each exterior angle measures 30°?

5. How many sides does a polygon have if the sum of the measures of the interior angles is 3960°?

6. If the sum of the measures of the interior angles of a polygon equals the sum of the measures of its exterior angles, how many sides does it have?

7. If the sum of the measures of the interior angles of a polygon is twice the sum of its exterior angles, how many sides does it have?

8. $\overline{XT}$ is the side of an equilateral triangle. $\overline{XS}$ is the side of a square. $\overline{XP}$ is the side of a regular pentagon. $\overline{XH}$ is the side of a regular hexagon. $\overline{XO}$ is the side of a regular octagon.

$m\angle TXS = $ _____ $m\angle SXP = $ _____

$m\angle PXH = $ _____ $m\angle HXO = $ _____

$m\angle OXY = $ _____

9. If the number of sides of a regular polygon doubles, what happens to the measure of each exterior angle?

10. Find each lettered angle measure.

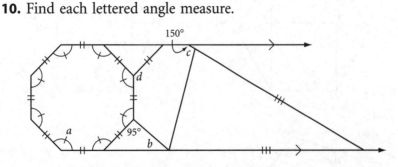

11. Construct an equiangular quadrilateral that is not regular.

12. Use a protractor and a ruler to draw a regular polygon.

Discovering Geometry Practice Your Skills
©2003 Key Curriculum Press

Lesson 5.3 • Kite and Trapezoid Properties

Name _____ Period _____ Date _____

In Exercises 1–4, find each lettered measure.

1. Perimeter = 116. $x =$ _____

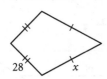

28   x

2. $x =$ _____, $y =$ _____

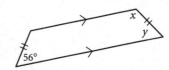

56° x y

3. $x =$ _____, $y =$ _____

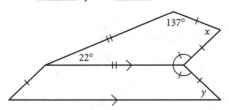

137° x
22°
y

4. $x =$ _____, $y =$ _____

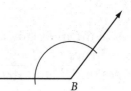

78°
41° x
y

5. Construct an isosceles trapezoid given base $\overline{AB}$, $\angle B$, and distance between bases XY.

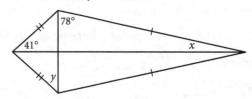

A •————————• B   X •———• Y

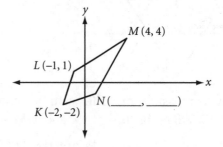

B

6. *STOP* is an isosceles trapezoid. What are the coordinates of *T*?

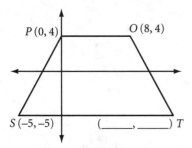

$P(0, 4)$ $O(8, 4)$

$S(-5, -5)$ (____, ____) T

7. *KLMN* is a kite. What are the coordinates of *N*?

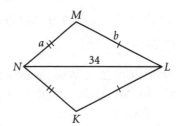

y
$M(4, 4)$
$L(-1, 1)$
x
$N($____, ____$)$
$K(-2, -2)$

8. Perimeter $PQRS = 220$. $PS =$ _____

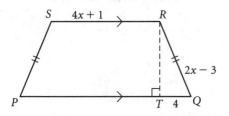

S $4x + 1$ R
$2x - 3$
P   T   4   Q

9. $b = 2a + 1$. $a >$ _____

M
a b
N   34   L
K

10. Construct kite $ABCD$ with $\overline{AB}$, $\overline{BC}$, and $\overline{BD}$.

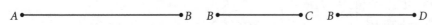

A •————————• B   B •————• C   B •————————• D

11. Write a paragraph or flowchart proof of the Converse of the Isosceles Trapezoid Conjecture.

Lesson 5.4 • Properties of Midsegments

Name _____ Period _____ Date _____

In Exercises 1–3, each figure shows a midsegment.

1. $a =$ _____, $b =$ _____,

$c =$ _____

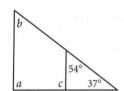

2. $x =$ _____, $y =$ _____,

$z =$ _____

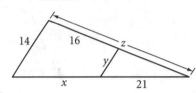

3. $x =$ _____, $y =$ _____,

$z =$ _____

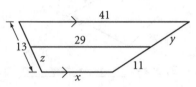

4. x, y, and z are midpoints. Perimeter $\triangle PQR = 132$, $RQ = 55$, and $PZ = 20$.

Perimeter $\triangle XYZ =$ _____

$PQ =$ _____

$ZX =$ _____

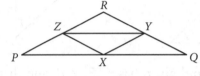

5. $\overline{MN}$ is the midsegment. Find the coordinates of M and N. Find the slopes of $\overline{AB}$ and $\overline{MN}$.

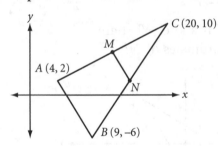

6. Explain how to find the width of the lake from A to B using a tape measure, but without using a boat or getting your feet wet.

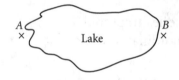

7. Find each measure, or write "cannot be determined." $DC = 68$, $AB = 44$, $BN = 15$, and $DM = 12$.

$MN =$ _____   Perimeter $ABCD =$ _____

$MP =$ _____ $m\angle DON =$ _____

$DP =$ _____ $m\angle A + m\angle B =$ _____

$m\angle B + m\angle C =$ _____

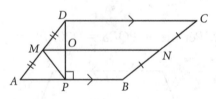

8. M, N, and O are midpoints. What type of quadrilateral is $AMNO$? How do you know? Give a flowchart proof showing that $\triangle ONC \cong \triangle MBN$.

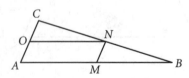

9. Give a paragraph or flowchart proof.

Given: $\triangle PQR$ with $PD = DF = FH = HR$
and $QE = EG = GI = IR$

Show: $\overline{HI} \parallel \overline{FG} \parallel \overline{DE} \parallel \overline{PQ}$

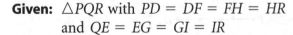

Discovering Geometry Practice Your Skills
©2003 Key Curriculum Press

Lesson 5.5 • Properties of Parallelograms

Name _____ Period _____ Date _____

In Exercises 1–7, *ABCD* is a parallelogram.

1. Perimeter *ABCD* = _____

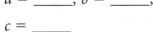

2. *AO* = 11, and *BO* = 7.

AC = _____, *BD* = _____

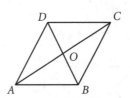

3. Perimeter *ABCD* = 46.

AB = _____, *BC* = _____

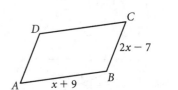
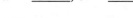

4. *a* = _____, *b* = _____,

c = _____

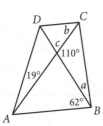

5. Perimeter *ABCD* = 119, and

BC = 24. *AB* = _____

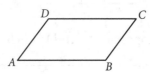

6. *a* = _____, *b* = _____,

c = _____

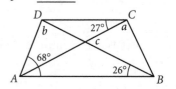

7. Perimeter *ABCD* = 16*x* − 12. *AD* = _____

8. If the diagonals of a quadrilateral are 15 cm and 9 cm, what is the perimeter of the quadrilateral formed by connecting the midpoints of the sides?

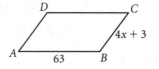

9. Construct a parallelogram with diagonals $\overline{AC}$ and $\overline{BD}$. Is your parallelogram unique? If not, construct a different (noncongruent) parallelogram.

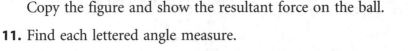

10. Ball B is struck at the same instant by two forces, $\vec{F_1}$ and $\vec{F_2}$. Copy the figure and show the resultant force on the ball.

11. Find each lettered angle measure.

12. If the perimeter of a parallelogram is 132 cm, the longest possible length of a diagonal is less than _____.

Lesson 5.6 • Properties of Special Parallelograms

Name _____ Period _____ Date _____

1. *PQRS* is a rectangle and
   OS = 16.

   OQ = _____

   m∠QRS = _____

   SQ = _____

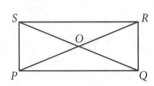

2. *KLMN* is a square and
   NM = 8.

   m∠OKL = _____

   m∠MOL = _____

   Perimeter *KLMN* = _____

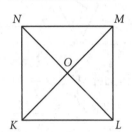

3. *ABCD* is a rhombus,
   AD = 11, and *DO* = 6.

   OB = _____

   BC = _____

   m∠AOD = _____

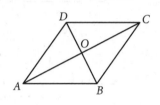

4. Construct rectangle *ABCD* with diagonal $\overline{AC}$ and ∠*CAB*.

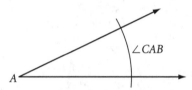

In Exercises 5–13, match each description with all the terms that fit it.

   a. Trapezoid   **b.** Isosceles triangle   **c.** Parallelogram   **d.** Rhombus

   e. Kite   **f.** Rectangle   **g.** Square   **h.** All quadrilaterals

5. _____ Diagonals bisect each other.

7. _____ Diagonals are congruent.

9. _____ Opposite sides are congruent.

11. _____ Both diagonals bisect angles.

13. _____ Has exactly one pair of congruent
   sides.

6. _____ Diagonals are perpendicular.

8. _____ Measures of interior angles sum
   to 360°.

10. _____ Opposite angles are congruent.

12. _____ Diagonals are perpendicular
   bisectors of each other.

In Exercises 14–17, determine whether quadrilateral *ABCD* with the given
coordinates is a trapezoid, parallelogram, rectangle, or none of these.

14. *A*(4, 0), *B*(12, 4), *C*(10, 8), *D*(2, 4)

16. *A*(−4, −1), *B*(0, −3), *C*(4, 0), *D*(−1, 5)

15. *A*(−5, −2), *B*(10, 3), *C*(6, 5), *D*(−3, 2)

17. *A*(2, −6), *B*(8, −2), *C*(0, 4), *D*(−6, 0)

18. *PQRS* is a square. What are the coordinates of *R* and *S*?

Discovering Geometry Practice Your Skills
©2003 Key Curriculum Press

Lesson 5.7 • Proving Quadrilateral Properties

Name _____ Period _____ Date _____

Write or complete each flowchart proof.

1. Given: $ABCD$ is a parallelogram and $\overline{BP} \cong \overline{DQ}$

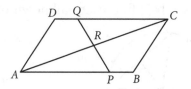

Show: $\overline{AC}$ and $\overline{PQ}$ bisect each other

Flowchart Proof

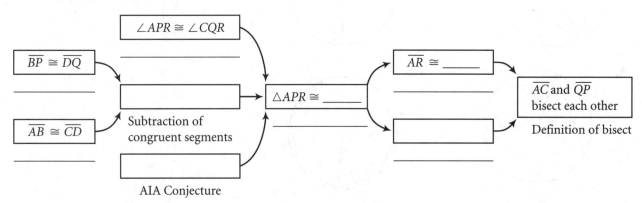

2. Given: Dart $ABCD$ with $\overline{AB} \cong \overline{BC}$ and $\overline{CD} \cong \overline{AD}$

Show: $\angle A \cong \angle C$

3. Show that the diagonals of a rhombus divide the rhombus into four congruent triangles.

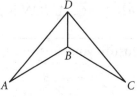

4. Given: Parallelogram $ABCD$ with angle bisectors $\overline{AX}$ and $\overline{CY}$

Show: $AXCY$ is a parallelogram

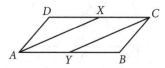

5. Given: Parallelogram $ABCD$, $\overline{BY} \perp \overline{AC}$, $\overline{DX} \perp \overline{AC}$

Show: $\overline{DX} \cong \overline{BY}$

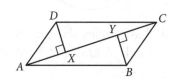

Lesson 6.1 • Chord Properties

Name _____ Period _____ Date _____

In Exercises 1–5, find each unknown or write "cannot be determined."

1.
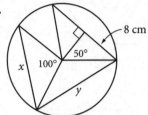

2.
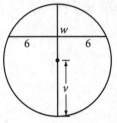

3.
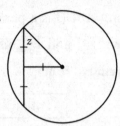

4.
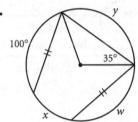

5.
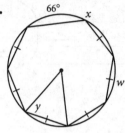

6. $\overline{AB} \cong \overline{AC}$. *AMON* is a _____.
Justify your answer.

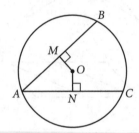

7. Trace part of a circle onto patty paper. Fold to find the center. Explain your method.

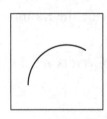

8. Find the coordinates of *P* and *M*.

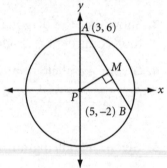

9. Two circles share a common chord. The chord cuts off a 70° arc of circle *A* and a 50° arc of circle *B*. Which circle has the larger radius?

10. $m\overarc{AB} =$ _____

$m\overarc{ABC} =$ _____

$m\overarc{BAC} =$ _____

$m\overarc{ACB} =$ _____

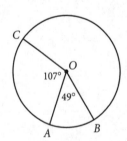

Discovering Geometry Practice Your Skills
©2003 Key Curriculum Press

Lesson 6.2 • Tangent Properties

Name _____ **Period** _____ **Date** _____

1. Rays *r* and *s* are tangents. *w* = _____

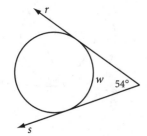

2. $\overleftrightarrow{AB}$ is tangent to both circles and $m\overparen{AMC} = 295°$. $m\angle BQX =$ _____

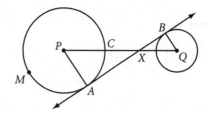

3. $\overleftrightarrow{PQ}$ is tangent to two externally tangent noncongruent circles, *M* and *N*.

  a. What kind of quadrilateral is *MNQP*? Explain your reasoning.

  b. If circles *M* and *N* are congruent, what is *MNQP*? Explain why.

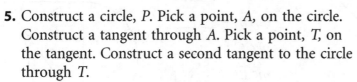

4. $\overleftrightarrow{AT}$ is tangent to circle *P*. Find the equation of $\overleftrightarrow{AT}$.

5. Construct a circle, *P*. Pick a point, *A*, on the circle. Construct a tangent through *A*. Pick a point, *T*, on the tangent. Construct a second tangent to the circle through *T*.

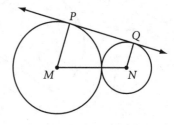

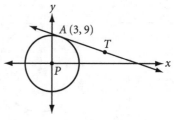

6. Circle *A* has diameter 16.4 cm. Circle *B* has diameter 6.7 cm.

  a. If *A* and *B* are internally tangent, what is the distance between their centers?

  b. If *A* and *B* are externally tangent, what is the distance between their centers?

7. $\overrightarrow{PA}$, $\overrightarrow{PB}$, $\overrightarrow{PC}$, and $\overrightarrow{PD}$ are tangents. Explain why $\overline{PA} \cong \overline{PD}$.

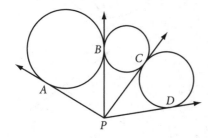

8. Circles *M* and *N* are tangent at *A*. $\overrightarrow{PA}$, $\overrightarrow{PB}$, and $\overrightarrow{PC}$ are tangents. Explain why $\angle PCB \cong \angle PBC$.

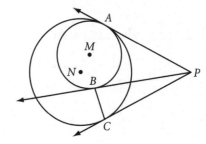

Lesson 6.3 • Arcs and Angles

Name _____ Period _____ Date _____

1. $m\widehat{XM} = 80°$

$m\angle XNM =$ _____

$m\widehat{XN} =$ _____

$m\widehat{MN} =$ _____

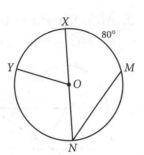

2. $\overleftrightarrow{AB}$ is a tangent.

$x =$ _____

$y =$ _____

$z =$ _____

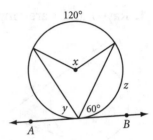

3. $a =$ _____

$b =$ _____

$c =$ _____

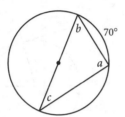

4. $a =$ _____

$b =$ _____

$c =$ _____

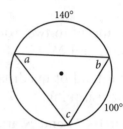

5. $\overrightarrow{AB}$ and $\overrightarrow{AC}$ are tangents.

$x =$ _____

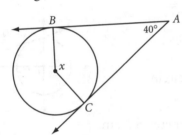

6. $\overrightarrow{AD}$ is a tangent. $\overline{AC}$ is a diameter.

$m\angle A =$ _____

$m\widehat{AB} =$ _____

$m\angle C =$ _____

$m\widehat{CB} =$ _____

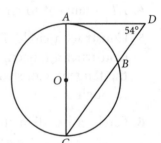

7. $m\widehat{AD} =$ _____

$m\angle D =$ _____

$m\widehat{AB} =$ _____

$m\widehat{DAB} =$ _____

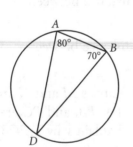

8. $p =$ _____

$q =$ _____

$r =$ _____

$s =$ _____

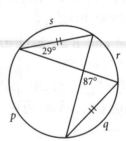

9. Find the lettered angle and arc measures.

$a =$ _____ $b =$ _____ $c =$ _____

$d =$ _____ $e =$ _____ $f =$ _____

$g =$ _____ $h =$ _____ $j =$ _____

$k =$ _____ $m =$ _____ $n =$ _____

$p =$ _____

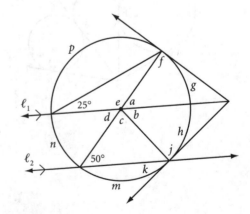

Lesson 6.4 • Proving Circle Conjectures

Name _____ Period _____ Date _____

In Exercises 1–3, complete each proof with a paragraph or a flowchart.

1. Given: Circle O with diameter $\overline{AB}$ and chord $\overline{AD}$. $\overline{OE} \parallel \overline{AD}$.

   Show: $\overparen{DE} \cong \overparen{BE}$

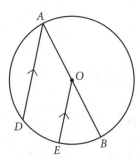

2. Given: Circles O and P are externally tangent, with common tangents $\overleftrightarrow{CD}$ and $\overleftrightarrow{AB}$

   Show: $\overleftrightarrow{AB}$ bisects $\overline{CD}$ at X

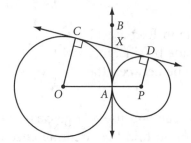

3. $\overleftrightarrow{PQ}$ and $\overleftrightarrow{RS}$ are tangent to both circles. Show that $\overline{PQ} \cong \overline{RS}$.

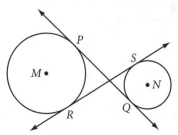

In Exercises 4–6, give a paragraph or flowchart proof for each statement.

4. If a quadrilateral is circumscribed about a circle, then the sums of the lengths of opposite sides are equal.

5. Prove the converse of the Chord Arcs Conjecture: If two arcs in a circle are congruent, then their chords are congruent.

6. If congruent chords in a circle intersect, then the point of intersection divides both chords in the same ratio.

Lesson 6.5 • The Circumference/Diameter Ratio

Name _____ Period _____ Date _____

In Exercises 1–7, leave your answers in terms of π.

1. If $r = 10.5$ cm, find C.

2. If $C = 25\pi$ cm, find r.

3. If $C = 9.6\pi$ cm, find d.

4. If $d = 12$ cm, find C.

5. What is the circumference of a circle whose radius is 30 cm?

6. What is the diameter of a circle whose circumference is 24π cm?

7. A square with sides that measure 2 cm is inscribed in a circle. Find the circumference of the circle.

In Exercises 8–13, round your answer to the nearest 0.1 unit. Use the symbol $\approx$ to show that your answer is an approximation.

8. If $d = 9.6$ cm, find C.

9. If $r = 8.1$ cm, find C.

10. If $C = 132$ cm, find d and r.

11. A dinner plate fits snuggly in a square box with perimeter 48 inches. What is the circumference of the plate?

12. Four saucers are part of the same set as the dinner plate in Exercise 11. Each has a circumference of 15.7 inches. Will they fit, side by side, in the same square box? If so, how many inches will there be between the saucers for padding?

13. $\overleftrightarrow{AT}$ and $\overrightarrow{AS}$ are tangents. $AT = 12$ cm. What is the circumference of circle O?

14. How can you use a large carpenter's square to find the circumference of a tree?

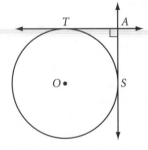

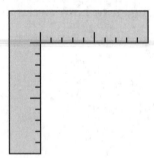

15. In order to increase the circumference of a circle from 16π cm to 20π cm, by how much must the diameter increase?

16. When a rock is dropped into a pond, a circular wave front spreads out from the point where the rock hit the water. If the wave moves out from the center at 0.7 m/sec, find the length of the wave front after 3 seconds. Round your answer to the nearest 0.1 m.

Discovering Geometry Practice Your Skills
©2003 Key Curriculum Press

Lesson 6.6 • Around the World

Name _____   Period _____   Date _____

1. Alfonzo's Pizzeria bakes olive pieces in the outer crust of its 20-inch (diameter) pizza. There is at least one olive piece per inch of crust. How many olive pieces will you get in one slice of pizza? Assume the pizza is cut into eight slices.

2. To use the machine below you turn the crank, which turns the pulley wheel, which winds the rope and lifts the box. Through how many rotations must you turn the crank to lift the box 10 feet?

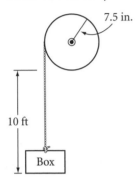

7.5 in.

10 ft

Box

3. A satellite in *geostationary* orbit stays over the same spot on Earth. The satellite completes one orbit in the same time that Earth rotates once about its axis (23.93 hours). If the satellite's orbit has radius 4.23×10^7 m, calculate the satellite's orbital speed (tangential velocity) in m/sec.

4. You can make an electromagnet by wrapping a wire around a nail and then sending a current through the wire. The strength of the magnet is directly proportional to the number of wrappings. The nail, pictured below, has a diameter of 0.4 cm. The wire is 0.05 cm in diameter, and you can get 100 wrappings side-by-side on the nail before having to start another layer. Consider each wrapping a perfect circle. How many meters of wire do you need, to the nearest 0.1 m, to make a magnet with 700 wrappings?

5. You want to decorate the side of a cylindrical can by coloring a rectangular piece of paper and wrapping it around the can. The paper is 19 cm by 29 cm. Find the two possible diameters of the can to the nearest 0.01 cm. Assume the paper fits exactly.

6. As you sit in your chair, you are whirling through space with Earth as it moves around the sun. If the average distance from Earth to the sun is 1.4957×10^{11} m and Earth completes one revolution every 364.25 days, what is your "sitting" speed in space relative to the sun? Give your answer in km/hr, rounded to the nearest 100 km/hr.

Lesson 6.7 • Arc Length

Name _____ **Period** _____ **Date** _____

Use your conjectures to solve each problem. Leave your answers in terms of π.

1. Length of $\overset{\frown}{AB}$ = _____

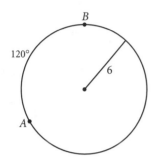

2. The circumference is 24π and $m\overset{\frown}{CD} = 60°$. Length of $\overset{\frown}{CD}$ = _____

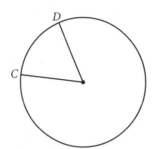

3. The length of $\overset{\frown}{EF}$ is 5π. Radius = _____

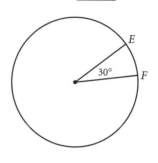

4. Length of $\overset{\frown}{XY}$ = _____

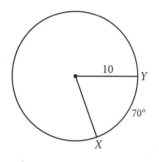

5. The radius is 20. Length of $\overset{\frown}{AB}$ = _____

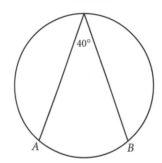

6. The circumference is 25π. Length of $\overset{\frown}{AB}$ = _____

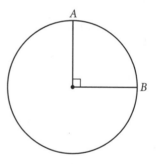

7. The diameter is 40. Length of $\overset{\frown}{AC}$ = _____

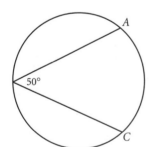

8. The length of $\overset{\frown}{XY}$ is 14π. Diameter = _____

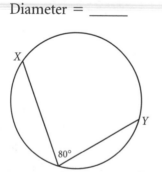

9. Length of $\overset{\frown}{AB}$ = _____

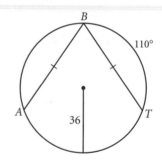

10. A circle has an arc with measure 80° and length 88π. What is the diameter of the circle?

Discovering Geometry Practice Your Skills
©2003 Key Curriculum Press

Lesson 7.1 • Transformations and Symmetry

Name _____ Period _____ Date _____

In Exercises 1–3, copy the figure onto graph or dot paper and perform the transformation.

1. Reflect △*TRI* over line ℓ.

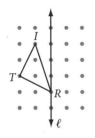

2. Rotate *PARL* 270° clockwise about *Q*.

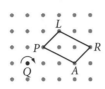

3. Translate *PENTA* by the given vector.

4. Copy *ABCDE* and its reflected image, *A′B′C′D′E′*. Use construction tools to locate the line of reflection, ℓ. Explain your method.

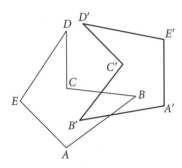

In Exercises 5–8, identify the type(s) of symmetry in each figure.

5. Equilateral triangle **6.** Rectangle   **7.** Isosceles triangle   **8.** Square

In Exercises 9–12, draw each polygon and identify the type(s) of symmetry in each. Draw all lines of reflection and mark centers of rotation.

9. Rhombus   **10.** Parallelogram   **11.** Isosceles trapezoid   **12.** Square

13. Copy △*ABC* and the center of rotation, *P*. Using only a compass and straightedge, construct the image of △*ABC* after a rotation of 180° about *P*.

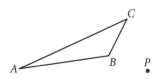

Lesson 7.2 • Properties of Isometries

Name _____ Period _____ Date _____

In Exercises 1–3, copy the figure and draw the image according to the rule.
Identify the type of transformation.

1. $(x, y) \rightarrow (-x, -y)$

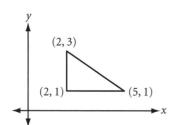

2. $(x, y) \rightarrow (x - 4, y + 6)$

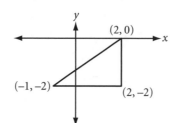

3. $(x, y) \rightarrow (4 - x, y)$

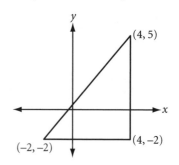

In Exercises 4 and 5, the Harbour High Geometry Class is holding a Fence
Race. Contestants must touch each fence at some point as they run from
S to *F*. Copy each diagram and use your geometry tools to draw the best
possible race path.

4.

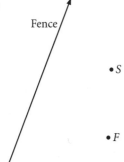

5.

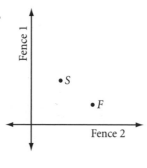

In Exercises 6–8, complete the ordered pair rule that transforms
each triangle to its image. Identify the transformation. Find all
missing coordinates.

6. $(x, y) \rightarrow ($ _____ , _____ $)$

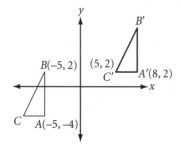

7. $(x, y) \rightarrow ($ _____ , _____ $)$

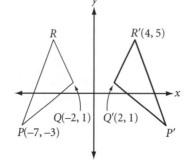

8. $(x, y) \rightarrow ($ _____ , _____ $)$

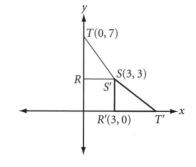

9. Give the inverse mapping rule (the rule that maps the image back to
the original) for each of the mappings in Exercises 1–3 and 6–8.

Lesson 7.3 • Compositions of Transformations

Name _____ Period _____ Date _____

In Exercises 1–8, name the single transformation that can replace the composition of each set of multiple transformations.

1. Translation by $(+4, +1)$, followed by $(+2, -3)$, followed by $(-8, +7)$

2. Rotation 60° clockwise, followed by 80° counterclockwise, followed by 25° counterclockwise all about the same center of rotation

3. Reflection over vertical line m, followed by reflection over vertical line n, where n is 8 units to the right of m

4. Reflection over vertical line p, followed by reflection over horizontal line q

5. Reflection over vertical line n, followed by reflection over vertical line m, where n is 8 units to the right of m

6. Reflection over horizontal line q, followed by reflection over vertical line p

7. Translation by $(+6, 0)$, followed by reflection over the y-axis

8. Reflection over the y-axis, followed by translation by $(+6, 0)$

In Exercises 9–12, copy the figure onto your paper and use your geometry tools to perform the given transformation.

9. Locate P', the reflected image over $\overrightarrow{OR}$, and P'', the reflected image of P' over $\overrightarrow{OT}$. Find $m\angle ROT$ and give a single transformation that maps P to P''.

10. Locate P', the reflected image over k, and P'', the reflected image of P' over ℓ. Find the distance between ℓ and k and give a single transformation that maps P to P''.

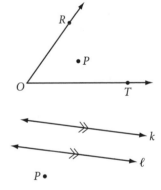

11. Draw five glide-reflected images of the triangle.

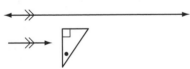

12. Using patty paper and dot paper, make three rotation-glide images of $\triangle ABC$. Find the first image by rotating the triangle 90° counterclockwise about point A and then translating by the rule $(x, y) \rightarrow (x + 4, y + 4)$. The second image is the image of the first image and so on.

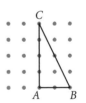

Lessons 7.4–7.8 • Tessellations

Name _____   Period _____   Date _____

1. Find *n*.

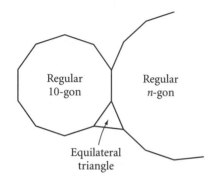

Regular 10-gon

Regular *n*-gon

Equilateral triangle

2. Find *n*.

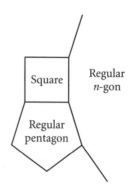

Square

Regular *n*-gon

Regular pentagon

3. What is a regular tessellation? Sketch an example to illustrate your explanation.

4. What is a 1-uniform tiling? Sketch an example of a 1-uniform tiling that is not a regular tessellation.

5. Use your geometry tools to draw the 4.8^2 tessellation.

6. Carefully draw the tessellation $3^6/3^2.4.3.4$ with your geometry tools. Draw the dual of the tessellation and identify the polygons in the dual. Calculate the measure of each angle in the dual.

7. Trace the quadrilateral at right (or draw a similar one). Make the outline dark. Set another piece of paper on top of the quadrilateral and, by tracing, create a tessellation. (Hint: Trace vertices and use a straightedge to connect them.)

8. Give the numerical name for the tessellation at right.

9. Use your geometry tools to draw a parallelogram. Draw squares on each side. Create a tessellation by duplicating your parallelogram and squares.

10. On dot paper, draw a small concave quadrilateral (vertices on dots). Allow no more than three dots inside the figure. Tessellate the entire paper with your quadrilateral. Color and shade your tessellation.

11. In *non-edge-to-edge tilings,* the vertices of the polygons do not have to coincide, as in these wooden deck patterns. Use graph paper to create your own non-edge-to-edge tiling.

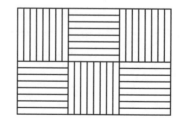

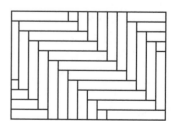

Discovering Geometry Practice Your Skills
©2003 Key Curriculum Press

Lesson 8.1 • Areas of Rectangles and Parallelograms

Name _____ Period _____ Date _____

1. Find the area of the shaded region.

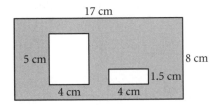

17 cm
5 cm
8 cm
1.5 cm
4 cm   4 cm

2. Find the area of the shaded region.

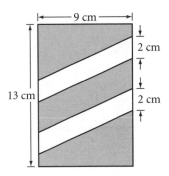

9 cm
2 cm
2 cm
13 cm
2 cm

3. Rectangle *ABCD* has area 2684 m² and width 44 m. Find its length.

4. Find *x*.

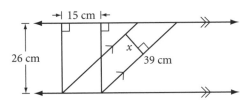

15 cm
26 cm
x
39 cm

5. The rectangle and the square have equal area. The rectangle is 12 ft by 21 ft 4 in. What is the perimeter of the entire hexagon in feet?

6. Draw a parallelogram with area 85 cm² and an angle with measure 40°. Is your parallelogram unique? If not, draw a different one.

7. Find the area of *PQRS*.

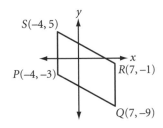

S(–4, 5)
P(–4, –3)
R(7, –1)
Q(7, –9)

8. Find the area of *ABCDEF*.

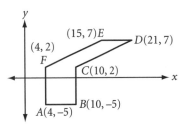

(15, 7)E
D(21, 7)
(4, 2)
F
C(10, 2)
A(4, –5)
B(10, –5)

9. An acre is equal to 43,560 ft². A 4-acre rectangular pasture has a 250-foot side that is 40 feet from the nearest road. To the nearest foot, what is the distance from the road to the far fence?

10. A *section* of land is a square piece of land 1 mile on a side. How many acres are in a section? (1 mile = 5280 feet)

11. Dana buys a piece of carpet that measures 20 square yards. Will she be able to completely cover a rectangular floor that measures 12 ft 6 in. by 16 ft 6 in.? Explain why or why not.

Lesson 8.2 • Areas of Triangles, Trapezoids, and Kites

Name _____ Period _____ Date _____

1. Find the area of the shaded region.

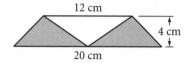

12 cm

4 cm

20 cm

2. *ABCD* is a parallelogram, *ABDE* is a kite, *AD* = 18 cm, and *BE* = 10 cm. Find the area of *ABCDE*.

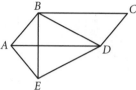

3. Area = 126 in.². *b* = _____.

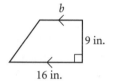

b

9 in.

16 in.

4. *AB* = 6 cm, *AC* = 8 cm, and *BC* = 10 cm. Find *AD*.

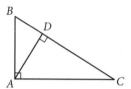

5. A concave kite (dart) has diagonals measuring 13 cm and 19 cm. What is its area?

6. The shaded area is what fraction of the large parallelogram?

7. Explain why the area of this triangle cannot be greater than 27.

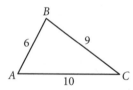

8. A midsegment of a triangle divides the triangle into a triangle and a trapezoid. If the original triangle has area 64 in.², what is the area of the trapezoid?

9. $\overline{TP}$ is tangent to circles *M* and *N*. *TP* = 16 cm. The radius of *N* is 7 cm and the radius of *M* is 4 cm. Find the area of *NMPT*.

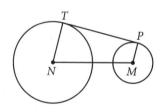

10. Find the area of △*TRI*.

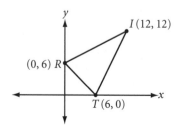

11. Find the area of *HEXAGN*.

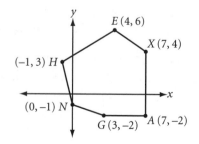

Discovering Geometry Practice Your Skills
©2003 Key Curriculum Press

Lesson 8.3 • Area Problems

Name _____ Period _____ Date _____

1. A bundle of hardwood flooring contains $14\frac{1}{2}$ ft² and costs $39.90. How much will it cost to buy flooring for the kitchen and family room? You should buy 5% extra to account for waste.

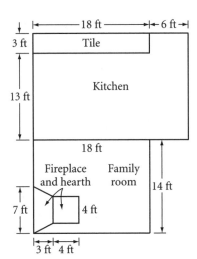

2. For a World Peace Day celebration the students at Cabot Junior/Senior High School are making a 6-m-by-8-m flag. Each of the six grades will create a motif to honor the people of the six inhabited continents. Sketch three possible ways to divide the flag: one into six congruent triangles; one into six triangles with equal area but none congruent; and one into six congruent trapezoids. Give measurements or markings on your sketches so each class knows it has equal area.

3. Olive has revolutionized the pizza industry by introducing square pizzas. She needs to charge $8.40 to recover her costs on a 12-inch (on a side) pizza. She then adds 25% and rounds up to the next multiple of a quarter. With this pricing scheme, what should Olive charge for a 16-inch pizza?

4. Bert's Bigtime Bakery has baked the world's largest chocolate cake. It is 600 cm by 400 cm by 180 cm high. Bert wants to apply frosting to the four sides and the top. How many liters of frosting does he need if 1 liter of frosting covers about 1200 cm²?

5. Jerome is making small metal kite pins to sell at the school fair. Each kite has an area of 24 cm² and one diagonal of 8 cm, which is divided by the other diagonal into 2 cm and 6 cm parts. The sheet metal comes in 27-cm-by-42-cm rectangles. How many kite pins can Jerome cut from one sheet? What percentage of waste does he have? Draw a cutting pattern Jerome could use.

6. Kit and Kat are building a kite for the big kite festival. Kit has already cut his sticks for the diagonals. He wants to position P so that he will have maximum kite area. He asks Kat for advice. What should Kat tell him?

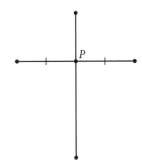

Lesson 8.4 • Areas of Regular Polygons

Name _____ Period _____ Date _____

In Exercises 1–3, the polygons are regular.

1. $s = 12$ cm and
$a \approx 14.5$ cm.

$A \approx$ _____

2. $s = 4.2$ cm and
$A \approx 197$ cm^2.

$a \approx$ _____

3. $a = 6$ cm and
$A \approx 130.8$ cm^2.

$p \approx$ _____

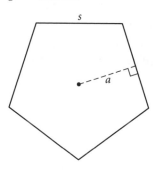

4. In a regular n-gon, $s = 4.8$ cm, $a \approx 7.4$ cm, and $A \approx 177.6$ cm^2. Find n.

5. A regular hexagon with side 8 cm has an area of approximately
166 cm^2. What are the diameters of the inscribed and the
circumscribed circles?

In Exercises 6–8, draw each regular polygon so that it has perimeter 20 cm.
Use the Regular Polygon Area Conjecture and a centimeter ruler to find
the approximate area of each polygon.

6. Pentagon

7. Octagon

8. Decagon

9. Use a compass and straightedge to construct a regular octagon and
its apothem. Use a centimeter ruler to measure its side length and
apothem and the Regular Polygon Area Conjecture to find its
approximate area.

10. Find the area of the shaded region between the square and
the regular octagon. $s \approx 5$ cm. $r = 3$ cm.

11. Copy the $3^2.6^2/3^6$ tessellation below showing the polygons
around each type of vertex. A regular hexagon with $s = 3$ cm
has $a \approx 2.60$ cm. An equilateral triangle with $s = 3$ cm has
$a \approx 0.87$ cm. If each side in this tessellation is 3 cm, find the
approximate area of each *dual* polygon.

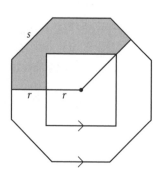

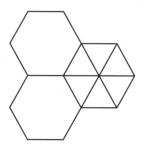

Discovering Geometry Practice Your Skills
©2003 Key Curriculum Press

Lesson 8.5 • Areas of Circles

Name _____ **Period** _____ **Date** _____

In Exercises 1–3, leave your answers in terms of π.

1. If $d = 6.4$ cm, $A =$ _____.
2. If $A = 529\pi$ cm^2, $r =$ _____.

3. If $C = 36\pi$ cm, $A =$ _____.

In Exercises 4–11, round your answers to the nearest 0.01 unit.

4. If $r = 7.8$ cm, $A =$ _____.
5. If $A = 136.46$, $C =$ _____.

6. If $d = 3.12$, $A =$ _____.

For Exercises 7 and 8, refer to the figure of a circle inscribed in an equilateral triangle.

7. Find the area of the inscribed circle.
8. Find the area of the shaded region.

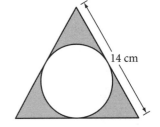

14 cm

9. $x = -2$ and $y = -1$ are tangent lines. *ABCD* is a square. Find the area of the shaded region.

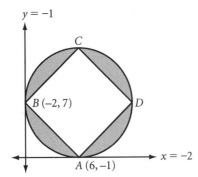

$y = -1$

C

B (–2, 7)

D

$x = -2$

A (6, –1)

10. A horse is tethered on a 20 ft rope. If the rope is lengthened to 25 ft, by what percentage does the horse's grazing area increase?

11. The three circles are tangent. Find the area of the shaded region.

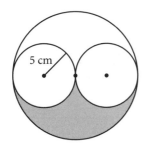

5 cm

12. A running track is shaped like a rectangle with a semicircle on each of the shorter sides. The distance around the track is 1 mile (5280 ft). The straightaway is twice as long as the width of the field. What is the area of the field enclosed by the track to the nearest square foot?

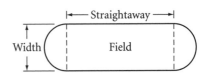

Straightaway

Width   Field

Lesson 8.6 • Any Way You Slice It

Name _____ **Period** _____ **Date** _____

In Exercises 1–6, find the area of the shaded region. Round your answers to the nearest 0.01 cm².

1.

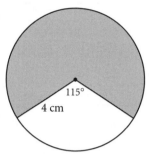

115°
4 cm

2.

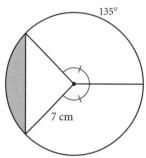

135°
7 cm

3.

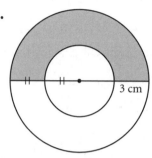

3 cm

4.

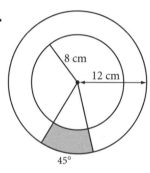

8 cm
12 cm
45°

5. $r_1 = 3$ cm, $r_2 = 6$ cm, and $r_3 = 9$ cm.

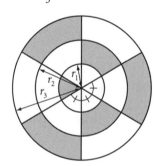

r_1
r_2
r_3

6.

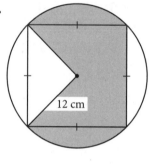

12 cm

7. Shaded area is 20π cm². Find r.

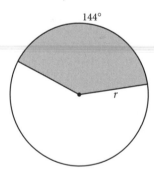

144°
r

8. Shaded area is 14 cm². Find r to the nearest 0.01 cm.

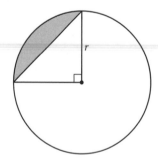

r

9. Shaded area is 15 cm². Find OT to the nearest 0.01 cm.

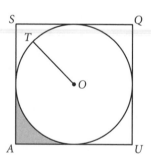

S Q
T
O
A U

10. Raul's dog, Spot, is tied with a 20 ft rope to the center of the back wall of the shed. See the diagram below. Over what area can Spot play, to the nearest square foot?

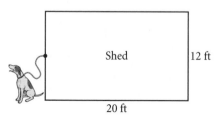

Shed
12 ft
20 ft

Discovering Geometry Practice Your Skills
©2003 Key Curriculum Press

Lesson 8.7 • Surface Area

Name _____ Period _____ Date _____

In Exercises 1–7, find the surface area of each solid. All quadrilaterals are rectangles, and all measurements are in centimeters. Round your answers to the nearest 0.1 cm².

1.

7
6
2

2. Base is a regular hexagon. $s = 6$, $a \approx 5.2$, and $l = 9$.
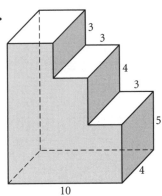
l
a
s

3.
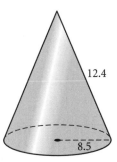
12.4
8.5

4.
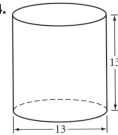
13
13

5.
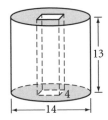
3
3
4
3
5
4
10

6. Both bases are squares.
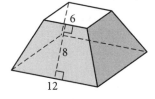
6
8
12

7. A square hole in a round peg
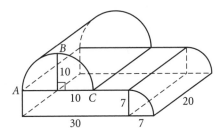
13
4
14

8. In order to calculate the heat loss of this restaurant, Kevin needs to find the area of the surface that is exposed to the air. $\overline{ABC}$ is a semicircle. All measurements are in feet. Round your answer to the nearest 0.1 ft².

B
10
A
10 C
7
20
30
7

9. Ilsa is building a museum display case. The sides and bottom will be plywood and the top will be glass. Plywood comes in 4-ft-by-8-ft sheets. How many sheets of plywood will she need to buy? Explain. Sketch a cutting pattern that will leave her with the largest single piece possible.

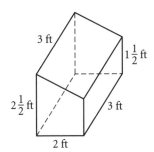
3 ft
$1\frac{1}{2}$ ft
$2\frac{1}{2}$ ft
3 ft
2 ft

Lesson 9.1 • The Theorem of Pythagoras

Name _____ Period _____ Date _____

Give all answers rounded to the nearest 0.1 unit.

1. $a =$ _____

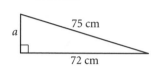
75 cm
a
72 cm

2. $p =$ _____

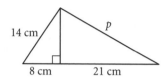
14 cm
p
8 cm   21 cm

3. $x =$ _____

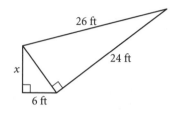
26 ft
24 ft
x
6 ft

4. Area = 39 in.²

$h =$ _____

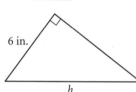
6 in.
h

5. Find the area.

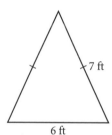
7 ft
6 ft

6. Find the coordinates of C and the radius of the circle.

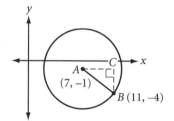
y
C
A
(7, −1)
x
B (11, −4)

7. Find the length of the diagonal. $P = 68$ cm and $A = 144$ cm².

Rectangle

8. Find the area.

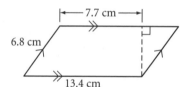
7.7 cm
6.8 cm
13.4 cm

9. $RS = 3$ cm. Find RV.

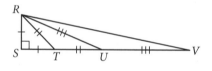
R
S   T   U   V

10. A regular decagon is inscribed in a circle with radius 6.7 cm. It has side length 4.14 cm. Find the length of the apothem.

11. Surface area = _____

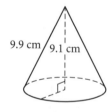
9.9 cm   9.1 cm

12. Base area = 16π cm² and slant height = 3 cm. What's wrong with this picture?

13. Given $\triangle PQR$, with $m\angle P = 90°$, $PQ = 20$ in., and $PR = 15$ in., find the area of $\triangle PQR$, the length of the hypotenuse, and the altitude to the hypotenuse.

14. Find the height of an equilateral triangular pyramid with side length 2 cm.

15. Find the length of the space diagonal of a box with dimensions 40 cm by 55 cm by 32 cm.

Discovering Geometry Practice Your Skills
©2003 Key Curriculum Press

Lesson 9.2 • The Converse of the Pythagorean Theorem

Name _____ **Period** _____ **Date** _____

All measures are in centimeters. Give answers rounded to the nearest 0.01 cm.

In Exercises 1–7, determine whether or not a triangle with the given side lengths is a right triangle.

1. 76, 120, 98

2. 221, 204, 85

3. $\sqrt{14}$, $\sqrt{30}$, 4

4. $1\frac{2}{3}$, $2\frac{2}{3}$, $3\frac{1}{3}$

5. 5.0, 1.4, 4.8

6. 80, 82, 18

7. 0.5, 1.2, 1.4

8. Determine whether or not A, B, and C are collinear. Explain your method.

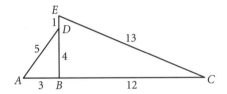

9. What's wrong with this picture?

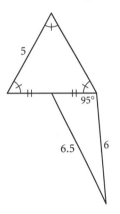

10. Find x. Explain your method.

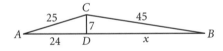

11. Find the area of $ABCD$.

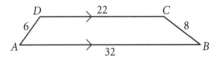

In Exercises 12–16, determine whether or not $ABCD$ is a rectangle. If not enough information is given, write "cannot be determined."

12. $AB = 3$, $BC = 4$, and $AC = 5$.

13. $AB = 3$, $BC = 4$, and $AC = 6$.

14. $AB = 3$, $BC = 4$, $DA = 4$, and $AC = 5$.

15. $AB = 3$, $BC = 4$, $CD = 3$, $DA = 4$, and $AC = BD$.

16. $AB = 3$, $BC = 4$, $CD = 3$, $AC = 5$, and $BD = 5$.

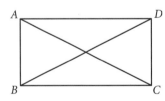

Lesson 9.3 • Two Special Right Triangles

Name _____ Period _____ Date _____

Give your answers in exact form unless otherwise indicated.

For Exercises 1 and 2, refer to △ABC.

1. If $BC = 60$, then $AC =$ _____, $AB =$ _____, and area $\triangle ABC =$ _____.

2. If $BC = 60\sqrt{2}$, then $AC =$ _____, $AB =$ _____, and area $\triangle ABC =$ _____.

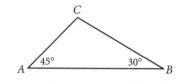

3. Find the perimeter and area of *KLMN*.

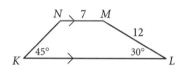

4. △ABC is equilateral. $AB = 18$. Find the area of *ABDE*.

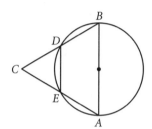

5. Find the area in terms of p, q, and r.

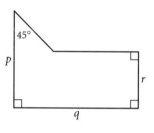

6. Find the area of an isosceles trapezoid if the bases have lengths 12 and 17 and the base angles have measure 60°.

In Exercises 7 and 8, find the coordinates of *C*.

7.

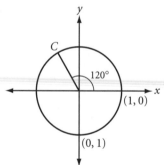

8.

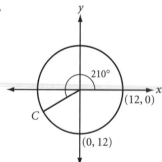

9. Construct a segment with length $2\sqrt{3}(AB)$.

10. Construct a square with area $5(AB)^2$.

11. Find the area of an 8-pointed star inscribed in a circle with radius 10 ft. Round your answer to two decimal places.

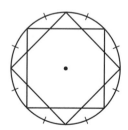

Lesson 9.4 • Story Problems

Name _____ Period _____ Date _____

1. A 20 ft ladder reaches a window 18 ft high. How far is the foot of the ladder from the base of the building? How far must the foot of the ladder be moved to lower the top of the ladder by 2 ft?

2. Robin and Dovey have four pet pigeons that they train to race. They release the birds at Robin's house and then drive to Dovey's to collect them. To drive from Robin's to Dovey's, because of one-way streets, they go 3.1 km north, turn right and go 1.7 km east, turn left and go 2.3 km north, turn right and go 0.9 km east, turn left and go 1.2 km north, turn left and go 4.1 km west, and finally turn left and go 0.4 km south. How far do the pigeons have to fly to go directly from Robin's house to Dovey's house?

3. Hans needs to paint the 18-in.-wide trim around the roof eaves and gable ends of his house with 2 coats of paint. A quart can of paint covers 175 ft² and costs $9.75. A gallon can of paint costs $27.95. How much paint should Hans buy? Explain.

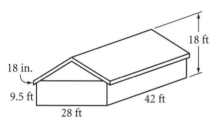

4. Ethel Diggs is at her base camp. She walks 3 km at a bearing of 50°. She turns and walks 4 km, and then turns and walks 5 km. She finds herself back at camp. What were the possible bearings of her 4 km leg?

Lesson 9.5 • Distance in Coordinate Geometry

Name _____ Period _____ Date _____

For Exercises 1 and 2, use $\triangle ABC$ with coordinates $A(4, 14)$, $B(10, 6)$, and $C(16, 14)$.

1. Determine whether $\triangle ABC$ is scalene, isosceles, or equilateral. Find the perimeter of the triangle.

2. Find the midpoints M and N of $\overline{AB}$ and $\overline{AC}$ respectively. Find the slopes and lengths of $\overline{MN}$ and $\overline{BC}$. How do the slopes compare? How do the lengths compare?

In Exercises 3–8, use the distance formula and the slope of segments to identify the type of quadrilateral. Explain your reasoning.

3. $A(-2, 1)$, $B(3, -2)$, $C(8, 1)$, $D(3, 4)$

4. $P(-2, 7)$, $Q(-3, -2)$, $R(6, -1)$, $S(7, 8)$

5. $K(7, 3)$, $L(0, 2)$, $M(-1, -5)$, $N(7, -5)$

6. $E(4, 0)$, $F(16, 4)$, $G(7, 7)$, $H(-5, 3)$

7. $W(17, -6)$, $X(9, 3)$, $Y(0, -5)$, $Z(8, -14)$

8. $T(-3, -3)$, $U(4, 4)$, $V(0, 6)$, $W(-5, 1)$

9. Find the equation of the circle whose diameter has endpoints $(4, -6)$ and $(-4, 0)$.

10. P is the center of the circle. What's wrong with this picture?

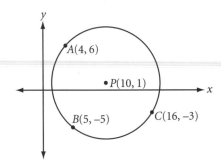

11. Given circle O with $O(3, -4)$ and radius 5, find 12 points on the circle with integer coordinates.

Discovering Geometry Practice Your Skills
©2003 Key Curriculum Press

Lesson 9.6 • Circles and the Pythagorean Theorem

Name _____ **Period** _____ **Date** _____

1. $AO = 7$. $AC = 8$. Find CB.

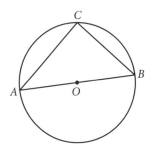

2. What's wrong with this picture?

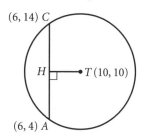

3. $MQ = 9$. $PS = 4$. Find PT, PT^2, and $(PS \cdot PQ)$. Explain why, in general, $PT^2 = PS \cdot PQ$.

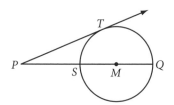

4. $AP = 63$ cm. Radius of circle $O = 37$ cm. How far is A from the circle?

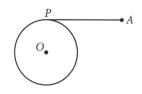

5. Two perpendicular chords with lengths 12.2 cm and 8.8 cm have a common endpoint. What is the area of the circle?

6. $ABCD$ is inscribed in a circle. $\overline{AC}$ is a diameter. If $AB = 9.6$, $BC = 5.7$, and $CD = 3.1$, find AD.

7. $\overline{AB}$ is a diameter, $AB = 8$, $AQ = 4$, and $AP = 8$. Find PR and PB.

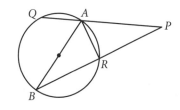

8. Find ST.

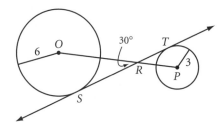

9. Find ST.

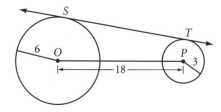

Lesson 10.1 • The Geometry of Solids

Name _____ Period _____ Date _____

For Exercises 1–14, refer to the figures below.

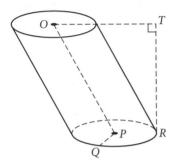 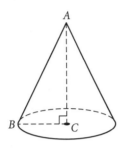 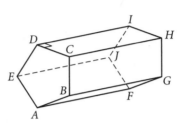

1. The cylinder is (oblique, right).

2. $\overline{OP}$ is _____ of the cylinder.

3. $\overline{TR}$ is _____ of the cylinder

4. Circles O and P are _____ of the cylinder.

5. $\overline{PQ}$ is _____ of the cylinder.

6. The cone is (oblique, right).

7. Name the base of the cone.

8. Name the vertex of the cone.

9. Name the altitude of the cone.

10. Name a radius of the cone.

11. Name the type of prism.

12. Name the bases of the prism.

13. Name all lateral edges of the prism.

14. Name an altitude of the prism.

In Exercises 15–19, tell whether each statement is true or false. If the statement is false, give a counterexample or explain why it is false.

15. The axis of a cylinder is perpendicular to the base.

16. The length of a lateral edge of a prism equals the altitude.

17. A rectangular prism has four faces.

18. A polyhedron with regular polygonal faces is a regular polyhedron.

19. The faces of a trapezoidal prism are trapezoids.

In Exercises 20–24, answer the question "What is _____ called?"

20. a regular triangular pyramid

21. a regular hexahedron

22. a solid with seven faces

23. the distance from the vertex to the plane of the base of a pyramid

24. a face that is not a base

Discovering Geometry Practice Your Skills
©2003 Key Curriculum Press

Lesson 10.2 • Volume of Prisms and Cylinders

Name _____ Period _____ Date _____

In Exercises 1–3, find the volume of each prism or cylinder.
All measurements are in centimeters. Round your answers to
two decimal places.

1. Right triangular prism

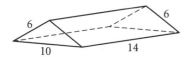

2. Right trapezoidal prism

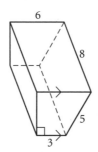

3. Regular hexagonal prism

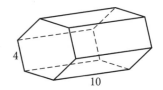

In Exercises 4–6, use algebra to express the volume of each solid.

4. Right rectangular prism

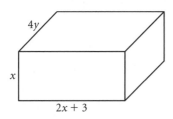

5. Right cylinder;
base circumference $= p\pi$

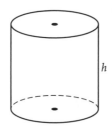

6. Right rectangular prism
and half of a cylinder

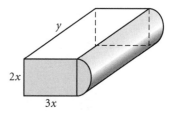

7. You need to build a set of solid cement steps for the entrance
to your new house. How many cubic feet of cement do
you need?

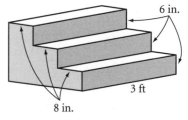

8. The foundation walls in the basement of your new house will be
8 in. thick and 6 ft high. The basement is 24 ft by 32 ft. The floor
is 4 in. thick. Under the walls is a 1-ft-wide-by-1-ft-deep footer.
Ignoring windows and doors, about how many cubic yards of
cement will you need for the walls, floor, and footer?

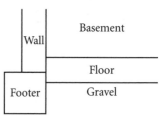

Lesson 10.3 • Volume of Pyramids and Cones

Name _____ Period _____ Date _____

In Exercises 1–3, find the volume of each solid. All measurements are in centimeters. Round your answers to two decimal places.

1. Rectangular pyramid; $OP = 6$

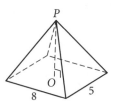

2. Right hexagonal pyramid

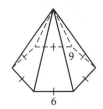

3. Half of a right cone

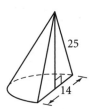

In Exercises 4–6, use algebra to express the volume of each solid.

4.

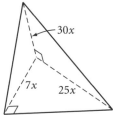

5.

6. The solid generated by spinning $\triangle ABC$ about the axis

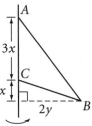

In Exercises 7–10, tell which volume is larger. Answer "C" if they are equal.

7. **A.**

B.

8. **A.**

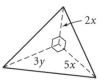

B.

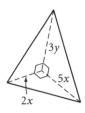

9. **A.**

B.

10. **A.**

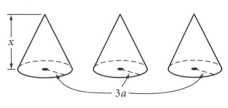

B.

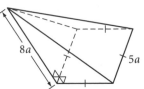

Discovering Geometry Practice Your Skills
©2003 Key Curriculum Press

Lesson 10.4 • Volume Problems

Name _____ Period _____ Date _____

1. The volume of a pyramid with an isosceles triangular base is 240 cm² and its height is 20 cm. The base of the base triangle is 6 cm. What is the length of the other two sides of the base?

2. A cylindrical oil drum holds 500 gallons. 1 cubic foot ≈ 7.5 gallons. If the diameter of the drum is 3.5 feet, about how high is it? Round your answer to 0.01 feet.

3. Use geometry tools to find the volume of one sheet of standard 8.5-in.-by-11-in. paper. Describe your method.

4. Jerry is packing cylindrical cans with diameter 6 in. and height 10 in. tightly into a box that measures 3 ft by 2 ft by 1 ft. All rows must contain the same number of cans. The cans can touch each other. He then fills all the empty space in the box with packing foam. How many cans can Jerry pack in one box? Find the volume of packing foam he uses. What percentage of the box's volume is filled by the foam?

5. Answer Exercise 4 for a box measuring 5 ft by 2 ft by 1 ft.

6. A square pyramid resting on its base is filled to half its height with 320 cm³ of water. How much water is needed to finish filling the pyramid?

7. A king-size waterbed mattress measures 72 in. by 84 in. by 9 in. Water weighs 62.4 pounds per cubic foot. An empty mattress weighs 35 pounds. How much does a full mattress weigh?

8. Square pyramid *ABCDE,* shown at right, is cut out of a cube with side length 2 cm to have the largest possible volume. Find the volume and surface area of the pyramid.

9. In Dingwall the town engineers have contracted for a new water storage tank. The tank is cylindrical with a base 25 ft in diameter and a height of 30 ft. One cubic foot holds about 7.5 gallons of water. About how many gallons will the new storage tank hold?

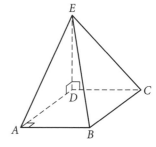

10. The North County Sand and Gravel Company stockpiles sand to use on the icy roads in the northern rural counties of the state. Sand is brought in by tandem trailers that carry 12 m³ each. The engineers know that when the pile of sand, which is in the shape of a cone, is 17 m across and 9 m high they will have enough for a normal winter. How many truckloads are needed to build the pile?

Lesson 10.5 • Displacement and Density

Name _____ Period _____ Date _____

1. A stone is placed in a 5-cm-diameter graduated cylinder, causing the water level in the cylinder to rise 2.7 cm. What is the volume of the stone?

2. A 141 g steel marble is submerged in a rectangular prism with base 5 cm by 6 cm. The water rises 0.6 cm. What is the density of the steel?

3. A solid wood toy boat with a mass of 325 g raises the water level of a 50-cm-by-40-cm aquarium 0.3 cm. What is the density of the wood?

4. For Awards Night at Baddeck High School, the math club is designing small solid silver pyramids. The base of the pyramids will be a 2-in.-by-2-in. square. The pyramids should not weigh more than $2\frac{1}{2}$ pounds. One cubic foot of silver weighs 655 pounds. What is the maximum height of the pyramids?

5. While he hikes in the Gold Country of northern California, Sid dreams about the adventurers that walked the same trails years ago. He suddenly kicks a small bright yellowish nugget. Could it be gold? Sid quickly makes a balance scale using his walking stick and finds that the nugget has the same mass as the uneaten half of his 330 g nutrition bar. He then drops the stone into his water bottle, which has a 2.5 cm radius, and notes that the water level goes up 0.9 cm. Has Sid struck gold? Explain your reasoning. (Refer to the density chart in Lesson 10.5 in your book.)

Lesson 10.6 • Volume of a Sphere

Name _____ Period _____ Date _____

In Exercises 1–4, find the volume of each solid. All measurements are in centimeters. Round your answers to 0.1 cm³.

1.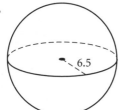

6.5

2.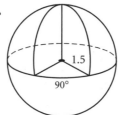

1.5

90°

3.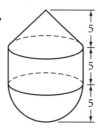

5

5

5

4. Cylinder with hemisphere taken out of the top

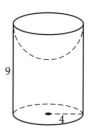

9

4

5. A sphere has volume $221\frac{5}{6}\pi$ cm³. What is its diameter?

6. A sphere has a great circle circumference of 40π ft. What is its volume?

7. The area of the largest section of a sphere is 225π in.². What is its volume?

8. A hemisphere has base area x cm² and volume x cm³. What is its radius?

In Exercises 9 and 10, find the volume of the solid generated by spinning each figure about the y-axis.

9. $m\overarc{ABC} = 90°$

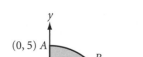

$(0, 5)\ A$

B

$C\ (5, 0)$

x

$(0, -3)\ E$

$D\ (5, -3)$

10. $\overarc{ABC}$ and $\overarc{DEF}$ are semicircles.

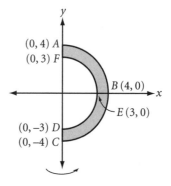

$(0, 4)\ A$

$(0, 3)\ F$

$B\ (4, 0)$

x

$E\ (3, 0)$

$(0, -3)\ D$

$(0, -4)\ C$

11. Eight wooden spheres with radii 3 in. are packed snuggly into a square box 12 in. on one side. The remaining space is filled with packing beads. What is the volume occupied by the packing beads? What percentage of the volume of the box is filled with beads?

12. The radius of Earth is about 6378 km, and the radius of Mercury is about 2440 km. About how many times greater is the volume of Earth than that of Mercury?

Lesson 10.7 • Surface Area of a Sphere

Name _____ Period _____ Date _____

In Exercises 1–4, find the volume and total surface area of each solid.
All measurements are in centimeters. Round your answers to the nearest
0.1 cm.

1.
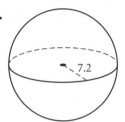

2.
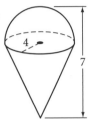

3.
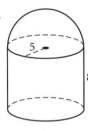

4.
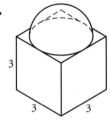

5. If the surface area of a sphere is 196π cm², find its volume.

6. If the surface area of a sphere is 48.3 cm², find its diameter.

7. If the volume of a sphere is 635 cm³, find its surface area.

8. If the surface area of a sphere equals the surface area of a cube, what is
the ratio of the volume of the sphere to the volume of the cube?

In Exercises 9 and 10, find the surface area of the solid generated by
spinning each figure about the *y*-axis.

9. $\overparen{ABC}$ and $\overparen{CDE}$ are semicircles.

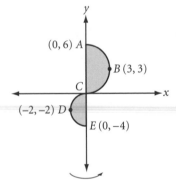

10. $m\overparen{ABC} = 90°$

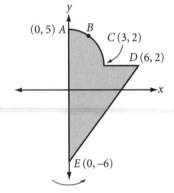

11. Lobster fishers in Maine often use spherical buoys to mark their lobster
traps. Every year the buoys must be repainted. An average buoy has a
12 in. diameter, and an average fisher has about 500 buoys. A quart of
marine paint covers 175 ft². How many quarts of paint does an average
fisher need each year?

Discovering Geometry Practice Your Skills
©2003 Key Curriculum Press

Lesson 11.1 • Similar Polygons

Name _____ Period _____ Date _____

All measurements are in centimeters.

1. *HAPIE ~ NWYRS*

$AP =$ _____

$EI =$ _____

$SN =$ _____

$YR =$ _____

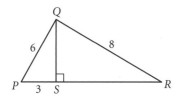

2. *QUAD ~ SIML*

$SL =$ _____

$MI =$ _____

$m\angle D =$ _____

$m\angle U =$ _____

$m\angle A =$ _____

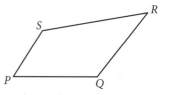
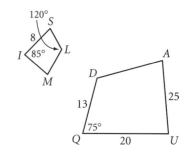

3. Copy *PQRS* onto your paper. Use a compass and straightedge to construct a similar quadrilateral with twice the perimeter of *PQRS*. Explain your method.

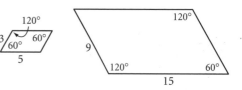

4. △*PQS ~ △QRS*. What's wrong with this picture? Explain.

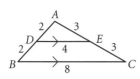

5. Are the pair of polygons similar? Explain why or why not.

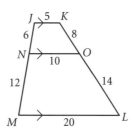

In Exercises 6–8, decide whether or not the figures are similar. If they are not, explain why.

6. △*ABC* and △*ADE*

7. *JKON* and *JKLM*

8. *ABCD* and *AEFG*

9. Copy *DART* and center *O* onto your paper. Use geometry tools to draw a dilation image with scale factor 1.5. Measure *DA*, *RT*, *D'A'*, and *R'T'*. Calculate $\frac{D'A'}{DA}$ and $\frac{R'T'}{RT}$. Are the results what you expected? Explain.

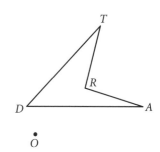

Lesson 11.2 • Similar Triangles

Name _____ Period _____ Date _____

All measurements are in centimeters.

1. △TAR ~ △MAC

MC = _____

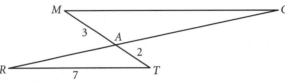

2. △XYZ ~ △QRS

∠Q ≅ _____

QR = _____

QS = _____

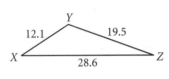

3. △ABC ~ △EDC

∠A ≅ _____

CD = _____

AB = _____

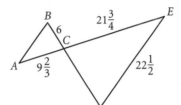

4. △TRS ~ △TQP

TS = _____

QP = _____

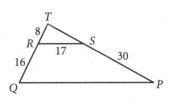

For Exercises 5 and 6, refer to the figure at right.

5. Explain why △CAT and △DAG are similar.

6. CA = _____

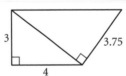

7. x = _____

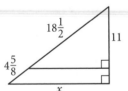

8. Are the two triangles similar? Explain why or why not.

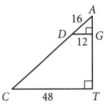

In Exercises 9–12, write an equation for two triangles that are similar. Explain why each pair is similar.

9.

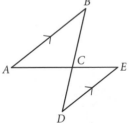

10.

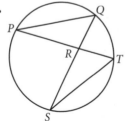

11.

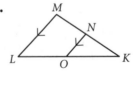

12.

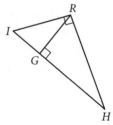

13. Draw a trapezoid with both diagonals. Name a pair of similar triangles.

Discovering Geometry Practice Your Skills
©2003 Key Curriculum Press

Lesson 11.3 • Indirect Measurement with Similar Triangles

Name _____ Period _____ Date _____

1. At a certain time of day, a 6 ft man casts a 4 ft shadow. At the same time of day, how tall is a tree that casts an 18 ft shadow?

2. If a 5 ft 10 in. person casts a 7 ft 4 in. shadow, how tall is a person who, at the same time, casts a 6 ft 8 in. shadow? Give your answer to the nearest inch.

3. Driving through the mountains, Dale has to go up and over a high mountain pass. The road has a constant incline for $7\frac{3}{4}$ miles to the top of the pass. Dale notices from a road sign that in the first mile he climbs 840 feet. What is the height of the mountain pass? (5280 ft = 1 mi)

4. Sunrise Road is 42 miles long between the edge of Moon Lake and Lake Road and 15 miles long between Lake Road and Sunset Road. Lake Road is 29 miles long. Find the length of Moon Lake.

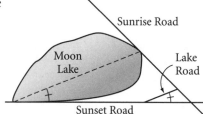

5. Marta is standing 4 ft behind a fence 6 ft 6 in. tall. When she looks over the fence, she can just see the top edge of a building. She knows that the building is 32 ft 6 in. behind the fence. Her eyes are 5 ft from the ground. How tall is the building? Give your answer to the nearest half foot.

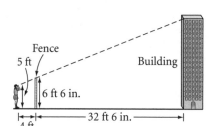

6. You need to add 5 supports under the ramp, in addition to the 3.6 m one, so that they are all equally spaced. How long should each support be? (One is drawn in for you.)

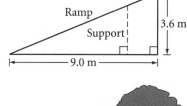

7. Stretch your arm out straight in front of you and hold your thumb straight up. Close one eye and look at a distant object. Without moving your arm (or thumb), switch eyes. What appears to happen? Measure the distance between your eyes and the distance between one eye and your thumb. Explain how, with one other piece of information, you can now use similar triangles to estimate the distance to the distant object. What else do you need to know?

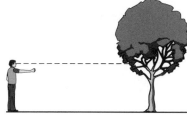

Lesson 11.4 • Corresponding Parts of Similar Triangles

Name _____ Period _____ Date _____

All measurements are in centimeters.

1. △ABC ~ △PRQ. M and N
are midpoints. Find h and j.

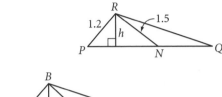

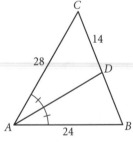

2. The triangles are similar.
Find the length of the three sides of the
smaller triangle to two decimal places.

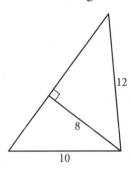

3. Median $\overline{AD}$ of △ABC has measure 12.4 cm. Median $\overline{A'D'}$ of the
dilation image △A'B'C' has measure 3.1 cm. If AB = 16.8 cm,
A'B' = _____.

4. △ABC ~ △WXY

WX = _____   AD = _____

DB = _____   YZ = _____

XZ = _____

5. BK = 6 cm, BL = 4 cm, and MN = 1 cm.
Find AC.

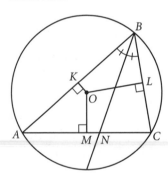

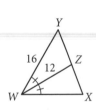

6. Draw a segment on your paper. Use construction tools to divide your
segment into two parts with ratio 3:5. Explain your method.

7. Find x and y.

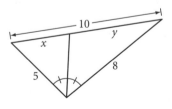

8. Find a, b, and c.

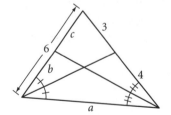

9. Find CB, CD, and AD.

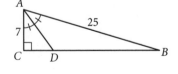

Discovering Geometry Practice Your Skills
©2003 Key Curriculum Press

Lesson 11.5 • Proportions with Area and Volume

Name _____ Period _____ Date _____

All measurements are in centimeters unless otherwise indicated.

In Exercises 1–4, decide whether or not the two solids are similar.

1.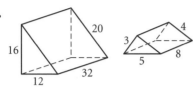

2.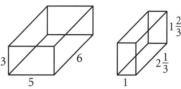

3.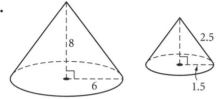

4.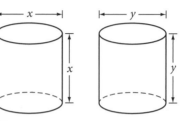

5. $\dfrac{\text{Area of square } SQUA}{\text{Area of square } LRGE} = $ _____

6. $\dfrac{\text{Area of circle } P}{\text{Area of circle } O} = $ _____

7. $RECT \sim ANGL$

$\dfrac{\text{Area of } RECT}{\text{Area of } ANGL} = $ _____

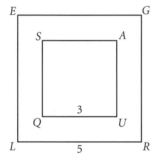

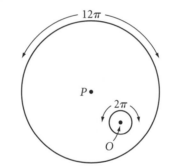

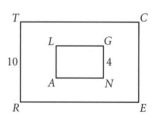

8. The ratio of the corresponding midsegments of two similar trapezoids is 4:5. What is the ratio of their areas?

9. The ratio of the areas of two similar pentagons is 4:9. What is the ratio of their corresponding sides?

10. The corresponding heights of two similar cylinders is 2:5. What is the ratio of their volumes?

11. The ratio of the weights of two spherical balls is 27:64. What is the ratio of their radii?

12. If $ABCDE \sim FGHIJ$, $AC = 6$ cm, $FH = 10$ cm, and area of $ABCDE = 320$ cm^2, then area of $FGHIJ = $ _____.

13. A rectangular prism aquarium holds 64 gallons of water. A similarly shaped aquarium hold 8 gallons of water. If a 1.5 ft^2 cover fits on the smaller tank, what is the area of a cover that will fit on the larger tank?

Name _____ Period _____ Date _____

All measurements are in centimeters.

1. $x =$ _____

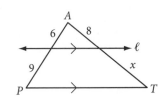

2. Is $\overline{XY} \parallel \overline{BC}$?

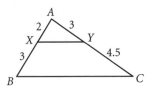

3. Is $\overline{XY} \parallel \overline{MK}$?

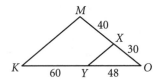

4. $NE =$ _____

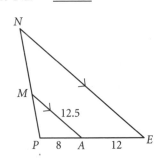

5. $PR =$ _____

$PQ =$ _____

$RI =$ _____

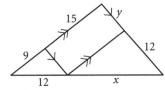

6. $a =$ _____

$b =$ _____

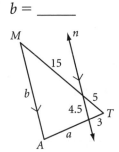

7. $RS =$ _____

$EB =$ _____

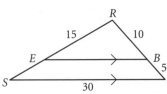

8. $x =$ _____

$y =$ _____

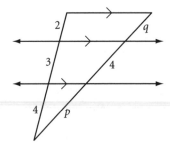

9. $p =$ _____

$q =$ _____

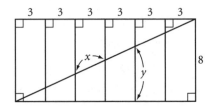

10. $x =$ _____

$y =$ _____

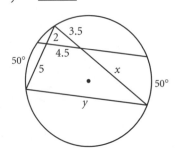

11. $AC =$ _____

$XY =$ _____

Explain why $m\angle YXB = 90°$.

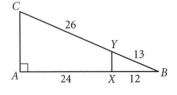

12. $x =$ _____

$y =$ _____

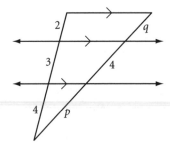

Lesson 12.1 • Trigonometric Ratios

Name _____ Period _____ Date _____

In Exercises 1–6, give each answer as a fraction in terms of p, q, and r.

1. $\sin P =$ _____   **2.** $\cos P =$ _____

3. $\tan P =$ _____   **4.** $\sin Q =$ _____

5. $\cos Q =$ _____   **6.** $\tan Q =$ _____

In Exercises 7–12, give each answer as a decimal accurate to three places.

7. $\sin T =$ _____   **8.** $\cos T =$ _____

9. $\tan T =$ _____   **10.** $\sin R =$ _____

11. $\cos R =$ _____   **12.** $\tan R =$ _____

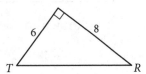

For Exercises 13–16, solve for x. Express each answer accurate to two decimal places.

13. $\cos 64° = \dfrac{x}{28}$ **14.** $\sin 24° = \dfrac{12.1}{x}$ **15.** $\cos 17° = \dfrac{143}{x}$ **16.** $\tan 51° = \dfrac{x}{14.8}$

For Exercises 17–20, find the measure of each angle to the nearest degree.

17. $\sin A = 0.9455$ **18.** $\tan B = \dfrac{4}{3}$ **19.** $\cos C = 0.8660$ **20.** $\tan D = \dfrac{4}{10}$

For Exercises 21–24, write a trigonometric equation you can use to solve for the unknown value. Then find the value to one decimal place.

21. $w \approx$ _____   **22.** $x \approx$ _____   **23.** $y \approx$ _____   **24.** $z \approx$ _____

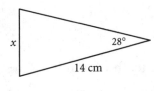
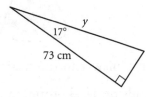
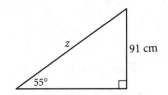

For Exercises 25–32, find the value of each unknown to the nearest tenth of a unit.

25. $a \approx$ _____   **26.** $f \approx$ _____   **27.** $t \approx$ _____   **28.** $h \approx$ _____

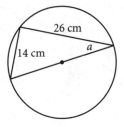
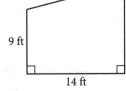
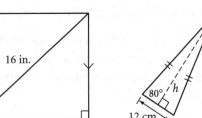

29. Regular pentagon with center O

   apothem $\approx$ _____

   radius $\approx$ _____

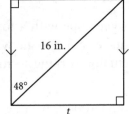

Lesson 12.2 • Problem Solving with Right Triangles

Name _____ Period _____ Date _____

For Exercises 1–4, find the area of each figure to the nearest square unit.

1. area ≈ _____ **2.** area ≈ _____ **3.** shaded area ≈ _____ **4.** area ≈ _____

50°
2.0 cm

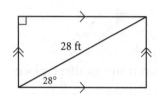
28 ft
28°

110° 41°
|← 11 cm →|

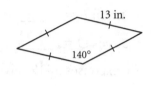
13 in.
140°

For Exercises 5–10, find each unknown to the nearest tenth of a unit.

5. area = 88 cm²

x ≈ _____

x
16 cm

6. y ≈ _____

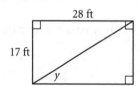
28 ft
17 ft
y

7. a ≈ _____

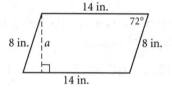
14 in.
72°
8 in. a 8 in.
14 in.

8. diameter ≈ _____

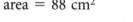
S
P
65°
22 cm
T

9. Right cone

θ ≈ _____

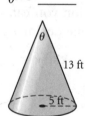
θ
13 ft
5 ft

10. m∠ABC = β ≈ _____

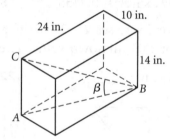
10 in.
24 in.
C
14 in.
β   B
A

In Exercises 11–16, give each answer to the nearest tenth of a unit.

11. A ladder 7 m long stands on level ground and makes a 73° angle with the ground as it rests against a wall. How far from the wall is the base of the ladder?

12. A monument is 116 m high and casts a shadow of 196 m. What is the angle of elevation of the sun?

13. Ben is pulling on a toboggan rope with a force of 250 newtons. The rope makes a 36° angle with the ground. What force is actually working to move the toboggan to the right?

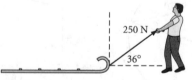
250 N
36°

14. To site the top of a building 1000 feet away, you look up 24° from the horizontal. What is the height of the building?

15. If a boat going 6 mi/hr in still water suddenly encounters a crosscurrent of 4 mi/hr, at what angle will the boat veer?

16. A guy wire is anchored 12 feet from the base of a pole. The wire makes a 58° angle with the ground. How long is the wire?

Discovering Geometry Practice Your Skills
©2003 Key Curriculum Press

Lesson 12.3 • The Law of Sines

Name _____ Period _____ Date _____

In Exercises 1–4, find the area of each figure to the nearest square unit.

1. area ≈ _____

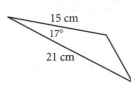
15 cm
17°
21 cm

2. area ≈ _____

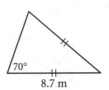
70°
8.7 m

3. area ≈ _____

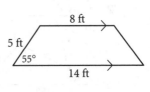
8 ft
5 ft
55°
14 ft

4. Regular hexagon

area ≈ _____

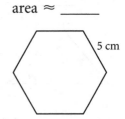
5 cm

In Exercises 5–8, find each length to the nearest centimeter. All measures are in centimeters.

5. m ≈ _____

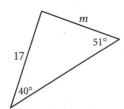
m
51°
17
40°

6. n ≈ _____

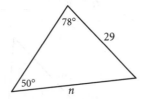
78°
29
50°
n

7. p ≈ _____

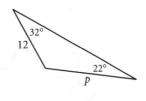
32°
12
22°
p

8. q ≈ _____

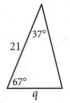
37°
21
67°
q

In Exercises 9–12, find the measure of each angle to the nearest degree.

9. m∠B ≈ _____

m∠C ≈ _____

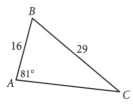
B
16
29
81°
A
C

10. m∠P ≈ _____

m∠Q ≈ _____

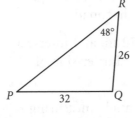
R
48°
26
P
32
Q

11. m∠K ≈ _____

m∠M ≈ _____

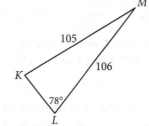
M
105
106
K
78°
L

12. m∠STU ≈ _____

m∠U = _____

m∠SVU = _____

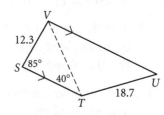
V
12.3
S
85°
40°
T
18.7
U

13. Find m∠B and m∠C to the nearest degree. Find the area of △ABC to one decimal place.

14. A large helium balloon is tethered to the ground by two taut lines. One line is 100 feet long and makes an 80° angle with the ground. The second line makes a 40° angle with the ground. How long is the second line, to the nearest foot? How far apart are the tethers?

15. Two angles of a triangle have measures 24° and 69°. The longest side of the triangle is 14.7 m. Find the lengths of the other two sides.

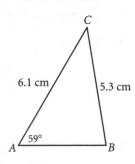
C
6.1 cm
5.3 cm
59°
A
B

Lesson 12.4 • The Law of Cosines

Name _____ Period _____ Date _____

In Exercises 1–4, find each length to the nearest centimeter. All lengths are in centimeters.

1. $t \approx$ _____

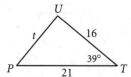

2. $b \approx$ _____

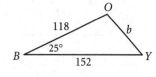

3. $w \approx$ _____

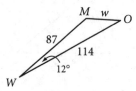

4. $a \approx$ _____

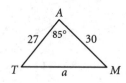

In Exercises 5–7, find each angle measure to the nearest degree.

5. $m\angle A \approx$ _____

$m\angle B \approx$ _____

$m\angle C \approx$ _____

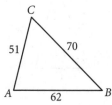

6. $m\angle A \approx$ _____

$m\angle P \approx$ _____

$m\angle S \approx$ _____

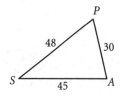

7. $m\angle S \approx$ _____

$m\angle U \approx$ _____

$m\angle V \approx$ _____

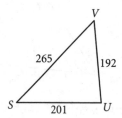

8. A circle with radius 12 in. has radii drawn to the endpoints of a 5 in. chord. What is the measure of the central angle?

9. A parallelogram has side lengths 22.5 cm and 47.8 cm. One angle measures 116°. What is the length of the shorter diagonal?

10. The diagonals of a parallelogram are 60 in. and 70 in. and intersect at an angle measuring 64°. Find the length of the shorter side of the parallelogram.

11. A triangular lot faces two streets that meet at an angle measuring 80°. The sides of the lot facing the streets are each 150 feet long. Find the perimeter of the lot.

12. Find l.

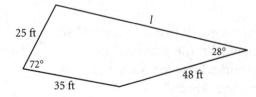

13. In a geometry game, a person with eyes closed starts at "home" and walks 5.0 m in a straight line, turns 130° counterclockwise, and walks 7.6 m in a straight line. How far is the person from "home"? Through what counterclockwise angle would the person turn to face "home"?

Discovering Geometry Practice Your Skills
©2003 Key Curriculum Press

Lesson 12.5 • Problem Solving with Trigonometry

Name _____ Period _____ Date _____

1. While floating down a river with a 2.75 mi/hr current, Alicia decides to swim toward the river bank. She can swim 0.75 mi/hr in still water. What is the actual speed at which she moves toward the bank? At what angle will she approach the bank, measured with respect to the bank?

2. Find the measure of each angle to two decimal places.

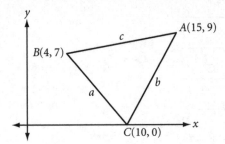

3. Two fire watchtowers 8.4 km apart spot a fire at the same time. Tower 1 reports the fire at a 36° angle measure from its line of site to Tower 2. Tower 2 reports a 68° angle measure between the fire and Tower 1. How far is the fire from each tower?

4. **a.** Express the cosine of angle A in terms of the sine of angle A.

   b. Use your answer to part a to find $\cos A$ without first finding the measure of $\angle A$. If $\sin A = 0.6820$, then $\cos A =$ _____.

5. Two airplanes leave O'Hare Airport in Chicago at the same time. One plane flies 280 mi/hr at bearing 55°. The other plane flies 350 mi/hr at bearing 128°. How far apart are the two planes after 2 hours 15 minutes?

6. On the 240-yard 4th hole of his municipal golf course, Lion Timber hits a tee shot 165 yards but 10° off the line to the flag. The cup is at the center of a circular green with a 30-foot radius. Find the range of distances Lion can hit the ball to land his second shot on the green.

7. Carla needs to fence her triangular plot of land. The angle between the two shorter sides measures 83°. The shortest side is 122 ft and the longest is 215 ft. How much fencing does Carla need? What is the area of her plot of land?

Lesson 13.1 • The Premises of Geometry

Name _____ Period _____ Date _____

1. Provide the missing property of equality or arithmetic as a reason for each step to solve the equation.

   Solve for x: $5(x - 4) + 15 = 2x + 17$

   Solution:

$5(x - 4) + 15 = 2x + 17$	**a.** _____
$5x - 20 + 15 = 2x + 17$	**b.** _____
$5x - 5 = 2x + 17$	**c.** _____
$3x - 5 = 17$	**d.** _____
$3x = 22$	**e.** _____
$x = \dfrac{22}{3}$	**f.** _____

In Exercises 2–5, identify each statement as true or false. If the statement is true, tell which definition, property, or postulate supports your answer. If the statement is false, give a counterexample.

2. If $AM = BM$, then M is the midpoint of $\overline{AB}$.

3. If P is on $\overleftrightarrow{AB}$ and D is not, then $m\angle APD + m\angle BPD = 180°$.

4. If $\overline{PQ} \perp \overleftrightarrow{AB}$ and $\overline{PR} \perp \overleftrightarrow{AB}$, then P, R, and Q are collinear.

5. If $\overline{PQ} \cong \overline{ST}$ and $\overline{PQ} \cong \overline{KL}$, then $ST = KL$.

6. Complete the flowchart proof. For each reason, state the definition, property, or postulate that supports the statement. If the statement is given, write "given" as your reason.

Given: $\overline{PQ} \cong \overline{RS}$, $\overline{PU} \cong \overline{QT}$, $\overline{RU} \cong \overline{ST}$

Show: $\angle P \cong \angle TQR$

Flowchart Proof

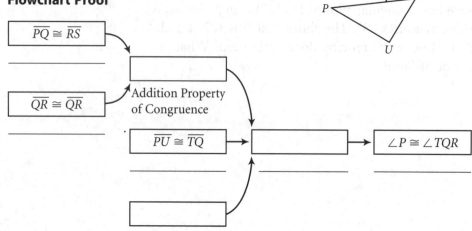

Lesson 13.2 • Planning a Geometry Proof

Name _____ Period _____ Date _____

For these exercises, you may use theorems added to your theorem list through the end of Lesson 13.2.

In Exercises 1–6, write a paragraph proof or a flowchart proof for each situation.

1. Given: $\overline{AB} \parallel \overline{CD}$, $\overline{AP} \parallel \overline{CQ}$

Show: $\angle A \cong \angle C$

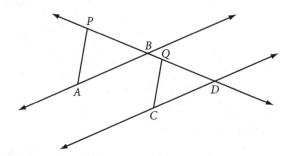

2. Given: $\angle B$ and $\angle ACB$ are complementary, $\angle DEF$ and $\angle F$ are complementary

Show: $\overline{BA} \parallel \overline{DE}$

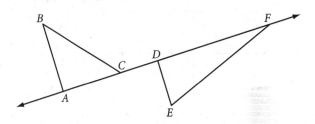

3. Given: $\overline{PQ} \parallel \overline{ST}$, $\angle QPR \cong \angle STU$

Show: $\overline{PR} \parallel \overline{UT}$

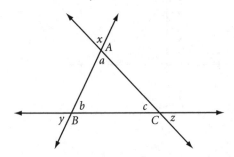

4. Given: $\overleftrightarrow{KL} \parallel \overleftrightarrow{QO}$, $\overleftrightarrow{KO} \parallel \overleftrightarrow{QP}$

Show: $\angle RKS \cong \angle TQU$

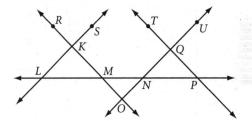

5. Given: Noncongruent, nonparallel segments AB, BC, and AC

Show: $x + y + z = 180°$

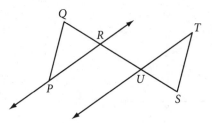

6. Given: Right angles A and P, $m\angle B = m\angle Q$

Show: $\angle DCB \cong \angle SRQ$

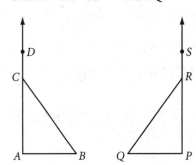

Lesson 13.3 • Triangle Proofs

Name _____ Period _____ Date _____

Write a proof for each situation. You may use theorems added to your
theorem list through the end of Lesson 13.3.

1. Given: $\overline{AB} \parallel \overline{CD}$, $\overline{AP} \parallel \overline{CQ}$, $\overline{PB} \cong \overline{QD}$
   Show: $\overline{AB} \cong \overline{CD}$

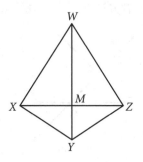

2. Given: $\angle BAC \cong \angle BCA$, M and N are
   midpoints of $\overline{AB}$ and $\overline{CB}$,
   respectively
   Show: $\angle AMC \cong \angle CNA$

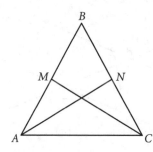

3. Given: $XY = ZY$, $\overline{XZ} \perp \overline{WY}$
   Show: $\triangle WXY \cong \triangle WZY$

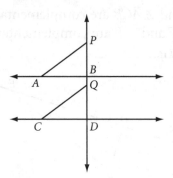

4. Given: $\overline{CD} \perp \overline{AC}$, $\overline{BD} \perp \overline{AB}$, $\overline{CD} \cong \overline{BD}$
   Show: $\triangle ABD \cong \triangle ACD$

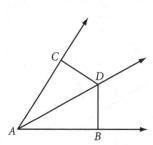

In Exercises 5 and 6, prove each statement using the given information
and diagram.

Given: $\overline{MN} \cong \overline{QM}$, $\overline{NO} \cong \overline{QM}$,
   P is the midpoint of $\overline{MO}$

5. Show: $\angle QMN \cong \angle RON$

6. Show: $\angle MPN$ is a right angle

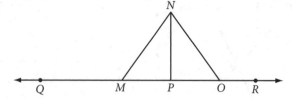

7. Given: $\overline{AB} \cong \overline{BC}$, $m\angle ACB = m\angle ECD$,
   $\overline{AB} \perp \overline{BD}$
   Show: $\overline{BD} \perp \overline{CE}$

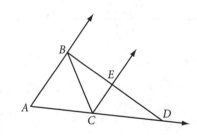

Lesson 13.4 • Quadrilateral Proofs

Name _____ Period _____ Date _____

In Exercises 1–6, write a proof of each conjecture. You may use theorems added to your theorem list through the end of Lesson 13.4.

1. The diagonals of a parallelogram bisect each other. (Parallelogram Diagonals Theorem)

2. If the diagonals of a quadrilateral bisect each other, then the quadrilateral is a parallelogram. (Converse of the Parallelogram Diagonals Theorem)

3. The diagonals of a rhombus bisect each other and are perpendicular. (Rhombus Diagonals Theorem)

4. If the diagonals of a quadrilateral bisect each other and are perpendicular, then the quadrilateral is a rhombus. (Converse of the Rhombus Diagonals Theorem)

5. If the base angles on one base of a trapezoid are congruent, then the trapezoid is isosceles. (Converse of the Isosceles Trapezoid Theorem)

6. If the diagonals of a trapezoid are congruent, then the trapezoid is isosceles. (Converse of the Isosceles Trapezoid Diagonals Theorem)

In Exercises 7–9, decide if the statement is true or false. If it is true, prove it. If it is false, give a counterexample.

7. A quadrilateral with one pair of parallel sides and one pair of congruent angles is a parallelogram.

8. A quadrilateral with one pair of parallel sides and one pair of congruent opposite angles is a parallelogram.

9. A quadrilateral with one pair of congruent opposite sides and one pair of parallel sides is a parallelogram.

Lesson 13.5 • Indirect Proof

Name _____ **Period** _____ **Date** _____

1. Complete the indirect proof of the conjecture: In a triangle the side opposite the larger of two angles has a greater measure.

   Given: $\triangle ABC$ with $m\angle A > m\angle B$

   Show: $BC > AC$

   Proof: Assume _____

   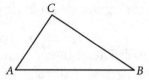

   Case 1: $BC = AC$

   If $BC = AC$, then $\triangle ABC$ is _____ by _____.
   By _____, $\angle A \cong \angle B$, which contradicts _____.
   So, $BC \neq AC$.

   Case 2: $BC < AC$

   If $BC < AC$, then it is possible to construct point D on $\overline{CA}$ such that $\overline{CD} \cong \overline{CB}$, by the Segment Duplication Postulate. Construct $\overline{DB}$, by the Line Postulate. $\triangle DBC$ is _____. Complete the proof.

   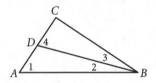

In Exercises 2–5, write an indirect proof of each conjecture.

2. **Given:** $\overline{AD} \cong \overline{AB}$, $\overline{DC} \not\cong \overline{BC}$

   Show: $\angle DAC \not\cong \angle BAC$

   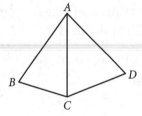

3. If two sides of a triangle are not congruent, then the angles opposite them are not congruent.

4. If two lines are parallel and a third line in the same plane intersects one of them, then it also intersects the other.

5. If a line is perpendicular to the radius of a circle at its outer endpoint, then the line is tangent to the circle. (Converse of the Tangent Theorem)

Discovering Geometry Practice Your Skills
©2003 Key Curriculum Press

Lesson 13.6 • Circle Proofs

Name _____ Period _____ Date _____

Write a proof for each conjecture or situation. You may use theorems
added to your theorem list through the end of Lesson 13.6.

1. If two chords in a circle are congruent, then their arcs are congruent.

2. Given: Regular pentagon *ABCDE* inscribed in circle *O*, with diagonals
$\overline{AC}$ and $\overline{AD}$

    Show: $\overline{AC}$ and $\overline{AD}$ trisect $\angle BAE$

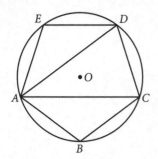

3. Write a generalization of the conjecture in Exercise 2 for any polygon.
(You don't need to prove it.)

4. Given: Two circles externally tangent at *R*, common external tangent
segment $\overline{TS}$

    Show: $\angle TRS$ is a right angle

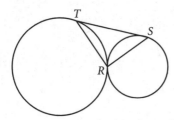

5. If two circles are externally tangent, their common external tangent
segments are congruent (two cases).

6. The perpendicular bisector of a chord contains the center of the circle.

7. Given: Two circles internally tangent at *T* with chords $\overline{TD}$
and $\overline{TB}$ of the larger circle intersecting the smaller
circle at *C* and *A*

    Show: $\overline{AC} \parallel \overline{BD}$

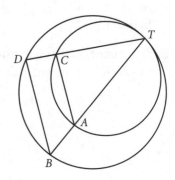

Lesson 13.7 • Similarity Proofs

Name _____ Period _____ Date _____

Write a proof for each situation. You may use theorems added to your
theorem list through the end of Lesson 13.7.

1. **Given:** $\triangle ABC$ with $\angle A \cong \angle BCD$

   Show: $BC^2 = AB \cdot BD$

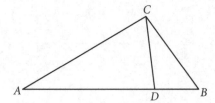

2. **Given:** Two circles externally tangent at R, $\overline{AB}$ and $\overline{CD}$ intersecting at R

   Show: $\dfrac{AR}{CR} = \dfrac{BR}{DR}$

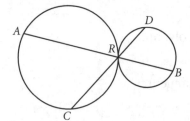

3. **Given:** Parallelogram $ABCD$, E is the midpoint of $\overline{CD}$

   Show: $CF = \dfrac{1}{3}AC$

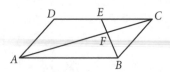

4. The diagonals of a trapezoid divide each other into segments with
   lengths in the same ratio as the lengths of the bases.

5. In a right triangle the product of the lengths of the two legs equals the
   product of the lengths of the hypotenuse and the altitude to the
   hypotenuse.

6. If a quadrilateral has one pair of opposite right angles and one pair of
   opposite congruent sides, then the quadrilateral is a rectangle.

Discovering Geometry Practice Your Skills
©2003 Key Curriculum Press

LESSON 1.1 · Building Blocks of Geometry

1. S **2.** 9 cm **3.** $\overline{SN}$ **4.** endpoint

5. $\overrightarrow{NS}$ **6.** $\overline{PQ}$ **7.** $\overrightarrow{SP}$

8. $\overline{KN} \cong \overline{KL},\ \overline{NM} \cong \overline{LM},\ \overline{NO} \cong \overline{LO}$

9.

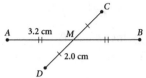

10.

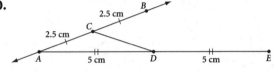

11. $E(-14, 15)$

12. $\overrightarrow{AB},\ \overrightarrow{AC},\ \overrightarrow{AD},\ \overrightarrow{AE},\ \overrightarrow{AF},\ \overrightarrow{BC},\ \overrightarrow{BD},$
$\overrightarrow{BE},\ \overrightarrow{BF},\ \overrightarrow{CD},\ \overrightarrow{CE},\ \overrightarrow{CF},\ \overrightarrow{DE},\ \overrightarrow{DF},$
$\overrightarrow{EF}$ (15 lines)

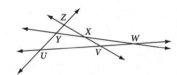

13. 2 lines

14. Possible coplanar set: $\{C, D, H, G\}$; 12 different sets

LESSON 1.2 · Poolroom Math

1. the vertex **2.** the bisector **3.** a side

4. 126° **5.** $\angle DAE$ **6.** 133°

7. 47° **8.** 63° **9.** 70°

10. 110° **11.**

12. **13.**

14. 90° **15.** 120° **16.** 75°

17. $m\angle APB$ would have to be 214°, which is larger than an angle measure can be.

18. First it increases, then it is undefined, then decreases, then undefined, then increases.

LESSON 1.3 · What's a Widget?

1. e **2.** d **3.** f **4.** c

5. g **6.** k **7.** b **8.** i

9. j **10.** l **11.** h **12.** a

13. Sample answers: sides of a road, columns, telephone poles

14. They have the same measure, 13°. Because $m\angle Q = 77°$, its complement has measure 13°. So, $m\angle R = 13°$, which is the same as $m\angle P$.

15.

16.
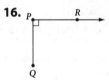

17.

LESSON 1.4 · Polygons

Polygon name	Number of sides	Number of diagonals
1. Triangle	3	0
2. Quadrilateral	4	2
3. Pentagon	5	5
4. Hexagon	6	9
5. Heptagon	7	14
6. Octagon	8	20
7. Decagon	10	35
8. Dodecagon	12	54

9. **10.**

11.

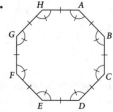

12. $\overline{AC}$, $\overline{AD}$, $\overline{AE}$

13. Possible answer: $\overline{AB}$ and $\overline{BC}$

14. Possible answer: $\angle A$ and $\angle B$

15. Possible answer: $\overline{AC}$ and $\overline{FD}$

16. 82°　　**17.** 7.2　　**18.** 61°　　**19.** 16.1

20. 12

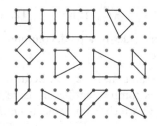

LESSON 1.5 • Triangles and Special Quadrilaterals

For Exercises 1–7, answers will vary. Possible answers are shown.

1. $\overline{AB} \parallel \overline{GH}$

2. $\overline{EF} \perp \overline{BI}$

3. $\overline{CG} \cong \overline{FH}$

4. $\angle EFH$ and $\angle IFH$

5. $\angle DEG$ and $\angle GEF$

6. $\angle DEG$ and $\angle GEF$

7. $\angle ADC$ and $\angle EDG$

8.

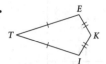

9.

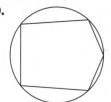

10.

11.

12.

For Exercises 13–25, answers may vary. Possible answers are shown.

13. *ACFD*　**14.** *ACIG*　**15.** *EFHG*　**16.** *EFIG*

17. *BFJD*　**18.** *BFHD*　**19.** *DHFJ*　**20.** *DFJ*

21. *ABD*　**22.** *ABD*　**23.** *D*(0, 3)　**24.** *E*(0, 5)

25. *F*(8, −2)　**26.** *G*(16, 3)

LESSON 1.6 • Circles

1.

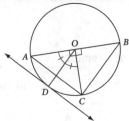

2. 48°　　**3.** 132°　　**4.** 228°　　**5.** 312°

6. 30°　　**7.** 105°　　**8.** $67\frac{1}{2}°$

9. The chord goes through the center, *P*. (It is the diameter.)

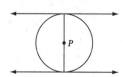

10.

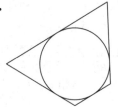

11.

12. (8, 2); (3, 7); (3, −3)

13.

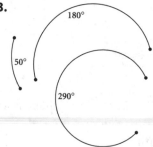

14. Kite

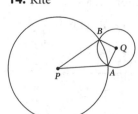

15.

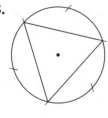

LESSON 1.7 • A Picture Is Worth a Thousand Words

1.

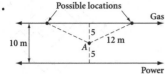

2.

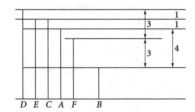

3. Dora, Ellen, Charles, Anica, Fred, Bruce

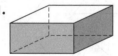

4. Possible answers:

a.   **b.**   **c.**

LESSON 1.8 • Space Geometry

1.   **2.**

3.

4. Rectangular prism   **5.** Pentagonal prism

6.   **7.**

8. Possible answer: **9.** Possible answer:

10. 18 cubes   **11.** $x = 2$, $y = 1$

LESSON 2.1 • Inductive Reasoning

1. 20, 24   **2.** $12\frac{1}{2}$, $6\frac{1}{4}$ **3.** $\frac{5}{4}$, 2

4. -1, -1 **5.** 72, 60   **6.** 243, 729

7. 485, 1457   **8.** 91, 140

9.

10.

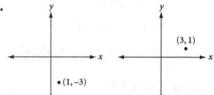

11.

12.

13. True   **14.** True   **15.** False; $\left(\frac{1}{2}\right)^2 = \frac{1}{4}$

LESSON 2.2 • Deductive Reasoning

1. No; deductive   **2.** 6, -2.5, 2; inductive

3. $m\angle E > m\angle D$ ($m\angle E = m\angle D + 90°$); deductive

4. a, e, f; inductive

5. Deductive

a. $4x + 3(2 - x) = 8 - 2x$	The original equation.
$4x + 6 - 3x = 8 - 2x$	Distributive property.
$x + 6 = 8 - 2x$	Combining like terms.
$3x + 6 = 8$	Addition property of equality.
$3x = 2$	Subtraction property of equality.
$x = \frac{2}{3}$	Division property of equality.

b. $\dfrac{19 - 2(3x - 1)}{5} = x + 2$ The original equation.

$19 - 2(3x - 1) = 5(x + 2)$ Multiplication property of equality.

$19 - 6x + 2 = 5x + 10$ Distributive property.

$21 - 6x = 5x + 10$ Combining like terms.

$21 = 11x + 10$ Addition property of equality.

$11 = 11x$ Subtraction property of equality.

$1 = x$ Division property of equality.

6. 4, 1, −4, −11, −20; deductive

7. a. 16, 21; inductive

b. $f(n) = 5n - 9$; 241; deductive

8. Sample answer: If any 3-digit number *"XYZ"* is multiplied by 7 · 11 · 13, then the result will be of the form *"XYZ,XYZ."* This is because 7 · 11 · 13 = 1001. For example,

$451 \cdot 7 \cdot 11 \cdot 13 = 451(7 \cdot 11 \cdot 13)$

$= 451(1001)$

$= 451(1000 + 1)$

$= 451{,}000 + 451 = 451{,}451$

LESSON 2.3 · Finding the *n*th Term

1. Linear   **2.** Linear   **3.** Not linear

4. Linear

5.

n	1	2	3	4	5	6
f(n)	−5	2	9	16	23	30

6.

n	1	2	3	4	5	6
g(n)	−10	−18	−26	−34	−42	−50

7. $f(n) = 4n + 5$; $f(50) = 205$

8. $f(n) = -5n + 11$; $f(50) = -239$

9. $f(n) = \frac{1}{2}n + 6$; $f(50) = 31$

10.

n	1	2	3	4	5	*n*	200
Number of tiles	1	4	7	10	13	3*n* − 2	598

11. *(See table at bottom of page.)*

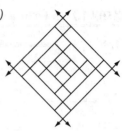

LESSON 2.4 · Mathematical Modeling

1.

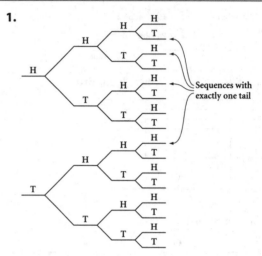

Sequences with exactly one tail

16 sequences of results. 4 sequences have exactly one tail. So, P(one tail) = $\dfrac{4}{16} = \dfrac{1}{4}$

2. 66 different pairs. Use a dodecagon showing sides and diagonals.

3. Possible answers:

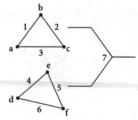

5 teams, 10 games

6 teams, 7 games

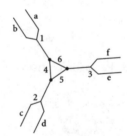

6 teams, 6 games

Lesson 2.3, Exercise 11

11.

Figure number	1	2	3	4	*n*	50
Number of segments and lines	2	6	10	14	4*n* − 2	198
Number of regions of the plane	4	12	20	28	8*n* − 4	396

LESSON 2.5 • Angle Relationships

1. $a = 68°$, $b = 112°$, $c = 68°$ 2. $a = 127°$

3. $a = 35°$, $b = 40°$, $c = 35°$, $d = 70°$

4. $a = 24°$, $b = 48°$

5. $a = 90°$, $b = 90°$, $c = 42°$, $d = 48°$, $e = 132°$

6. $a = 20°$, $b = 70°$, $c = 20°$, $d = 70°$, $e = 110°$

7. $a = 70°$, $b = 55°$, $c = 25°$

8. $a = 90°$, $b = 90°$ 9. Sometimes

10. Always   11. Never   12. Always

13. Never   14. Sometimes 15. acute

16. 158°   17. 90°   18. obtuse

19. converse

LESSON 2.6 • Special Angles on Parallel Lines

1. One of: ∠1 and ∠3; ∠5 and ∠7; ∠2 and ∠4; ∠6 and ∠8

2. One of: ∠2 and ∠7; ∠3 and ∠6

3. One of: ∠1 and ∠8; ∠4 and ∠5

4. One of: ∠1 and ∠6; ∠3 and ∠8; ∠2 and ∠5; ∠4 and ∠7

5. One of: ∠1 and ∠2; ∠3 and ∠4; ∠5 and ∠6; ∠7 and ∠8; ∠1 and ∠5; ∠2 and ∠6; ∠3 and ∠7; ∠4 and ∠8

6. Sometimes   7. Always   8. Always

9. Always   10. Never   11. Sometimes

12. $a = 54°$, $b = 54°$, $c = 54°$

13. $a = 115°$, $b = 65°$, $c = 115°$, $d = 65°$

14. $a = 72°$, $b = 126°$ 15. $\ell_1 \parallel \ell_2$

16. $\ell_1 \nparallel \ell_2$ 17. cannot be determined

18. $a = 102°$, $b = 78°$, $c = 58°$, $d = 122°$, $e = 26°$, $f = 58°$

LESSON 3.1 • Duplicating Segments and Angles

1.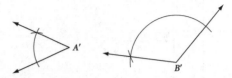

2. $XY = 3PQ - 2RS$

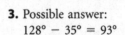

3. Possible answer:
128° − 35° = 93°

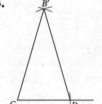

4.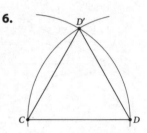

5. 6.

6.

7. Four possible triangles. One is shown below.

LESSON 3.2 • Constructing Perpendicular Bisectors

1.   2. Square

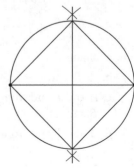

3. $XY = \frac{5}{4}AB$

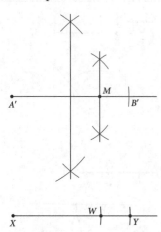

4. midpoint P of $\overline{AB}$ is (4.5, 0); midpoint Q of $\overline{BC}$ is (7.5, 6); midpoint R of $\overline{AC}$ is (3, 6); slope $\overline{PQ} = 2$; slope $\overline{QR} = 0$; slope $\overline{PR} = -4$.

5. $\triangle ABC$ is not unique.

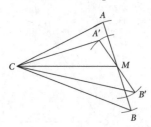

6. $\triangle ABC$ is not unique.

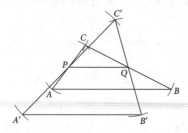

7. $BD = AD = CD$

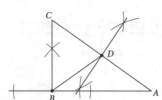

8. a. A and B

  b. A, B, and C

  c. A and B and from C and D (but not from B and C)

  d. A and B and from E and D

LESSON 3.3 • Constructing Perpendiculars to a Line

1. False. The altitude from A coincides with the side so it is not shorter.

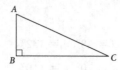

2. False. In an isosceles triangle, an altitude and median coincide so they are of equal length.

3. True

4. False. In an acute triangle, all altitudes are inside. In a right triangle, one altitude is inside and two are sides. In an obtuse triangle, one altitude is inside and two are outside. There is no other possibility so exactly one altitude is never outside.

5. False. In an obtuse triangle, the intersection of the perpendicular bisectors is outside the triangle.

6.

7.

8. $WX = YZ$

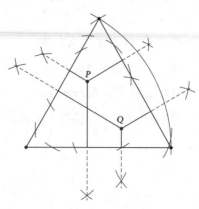
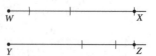

Discovering Geometry Practice Your Skills
©2003 Key Curriculum Press

LESSON 3.4 • Constructing Angle Bisectors

1.

 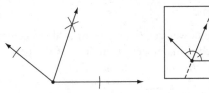

2. They are concurrent.

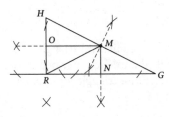

3. a. ℓ_1 and ℓ_2

b. ℓ_1, ℓ_2, and ℓ_3

c. ℓ_2, ℓ_3, and ℓ_4

d. ℓ_1 and ℓ_2 and from ℓ_3 and ℓ_4

4. $\overrightarrow{AP}$ is the bisector of $\angle CAB$

5. $RN = GN$ and $RO = HO$

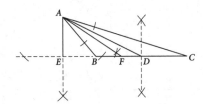

6. $AC > AD > AF > AB > AE$ or
$AB > AD > AF > AC > AE$
(B and C are reversed.)

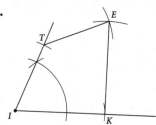

LESSON 3.5 • Constructing Parallel Lines

1.

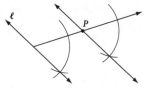

2.

3.

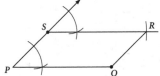

4.

5.

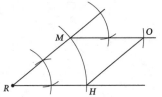

6. Possible answer:

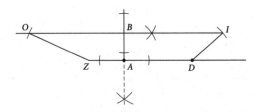

7. Cannot be determined   **8.** True

9. True   **10.** False   **11.** True

12. Cannot be determined   **13.** True

14. False   **15.** True

LESSON 3.6 • Construction Problems

1.

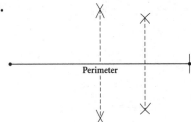

2.

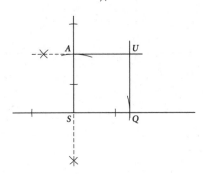

3.

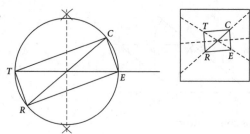

4.

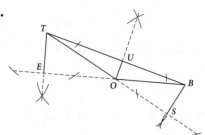

5.

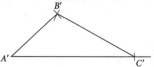

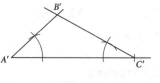

6. Possible answer:

7. Possible answer:

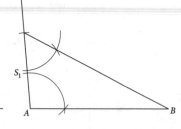

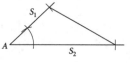

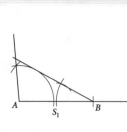

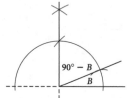

8.

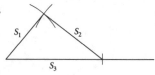

LESSON 3.7 • Constructing Points of Concurrency

1. Circumcenter

2. Locate the power-generation plant at the incenter. Locate each transformer at the foot of the perpendicular from the incenter to each side.

3.

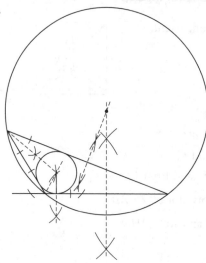

4. Possible answers: In the equilateral triangle, the centers of the inscribed and circumscribed circles are the same. In the obtuse triangle, one center is outside the triangle.

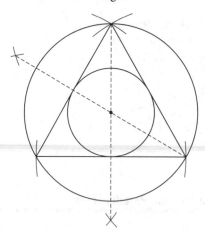

5.

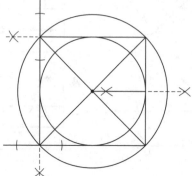

6. Possible answer: In an acute triangle, the circumcenter is inside the triangle. In a right triangle, it is on the hypotenuse. In an obtuse triangle, the circumcenter is outside the triangle. (Constructions not shown.)

LESSON 3.8 · The Centroid

1.

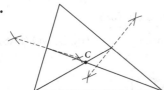

2.

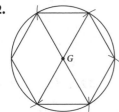

3. $CP = 3.3$ cm, $CQ = 5.7$ cm, $CR = 4.8$ cm

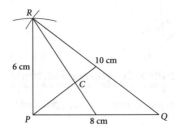

4. (3, 4)

5. $PC = 16$, $CL = 8$, $QM = 15$, $CR = 14$

6. a. Incenter   **b.** Centroid
   c. Circumcenter   **d.** Circumcenter
   e. Orthocenter   **f.** Incenter
   g. Centroid   **h.** Centroid
   i. Circumcenter   **j.** Orthocenter

LESSON 4.1 · Triangle Sum Conjecture

1. $p = 67°$, $q = 15°$ **2.** $x = 82°$, $y = 81°$

3. $a = 78°$, $b = 29°$

4. $r = 40°$, $s = 40°$, $t = 100°$

5. $x = 31°$, $y = 64°$ **6.** $y = 145°$

7. $s = 28°$ **8.** $m = 72\frac{1}{2}°$

9. $m\angle P = a$

10. The sum of the measures of $\angle A$ and $\angle B$ is 90° because $m\angle C$ is 90° and all three angles must be 180°. So, $\angle A$ and $\angle B$ are complementary.

11. 720°

12. $m\angle BEA = m\angle CED$ because they are vertical angles. Because the measures of all three angles in each triangle add to 180°, if equal measures are subtracted from each, what remains will be equal.

13. $m\angle QPT = 135°$ **14.** $m\angle ADB = 115°$

LESSON 4.2 · Properties of Special Triangles

1. $m\angle T = 64°$ **2.** $m\angle G = 45°$

3. $x = 125°$

4. a. $\angle A \cong \angle ABD \cong \angle DBC \cong \angle BDC$
   b. $\overline{BC} \cong \overline{DC}$

5. a. $\angle DAB \cong \angle ABD \cong \angle BDC \cong \angle BCD$
   b. $\angle ADB \cong \angle CBD$
   c. $\overline{AD} \parallel \overline{BC}$ by the Converse of the AIA Conjecture.

6. $m\angle PRQ = 55°$ by VA, which makes $m\angle P = 55°$ by the Triangle Sum Conjecture. So, $\triangle PQR$ is isosceles by the Converse of the Isosceles Triangle Conjecture.

7. $x = 21°$, $y = 16°$ **8.** $m\angle QPR = 15°$

9. $\angle CGI \cong \angle CIG \cong \angle CAE \cong \angle CEA \cong \angle FIE \cong \angle JED \cong \angle FJE \cong \angle BJH \cong \angle BHJ$. Because $\angle BJH \cong \angle BHJ$, $\triangle JBH$ is isosceles by the Converse of the Isosceles Triangle Conjecture.

10. Possible method: $m\angle PQR = 60°$: construction of equilateral triangle; $m\angle PQS = 30°$: bisection of $\angle PQR$; $\angle A \cong \angle PQS$: angle duplication; mark $AC = AB$; base angles B and C measure 75°.

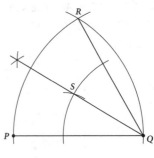

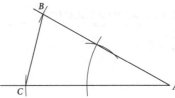

11. (5, 6)   **12.** $B(1, -1)$, $C(-2, 6)$

LESSON 4.3 · Triangle Inequalities

1. Yes

2. No

3. Yes

4. No

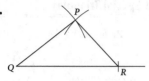

5. Not possible. $AB + BC < AC$

6.

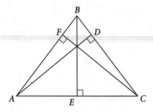

7. $19 < x < 53$ **8.** $b > a > c$

9. $b > c > a$ **10.** $d > e > c > b > a$

11. $a > c = d > b$ **12.** $c > b > a$

13. $c > a > b$ **14.** $x = 76°$

15. $x = 79°$

16. The interior angle at A is 60°. The interior angle at B is 20°. But now the sum of the measures of the triangle is not 180°.

17. By the Exterior Angles Conjecture, $2x = x + m\angle PQS$. So, $m\angle PQS = x$. So, by the Converse of the Isosceles Triangle Conjecture, $\angle PQS$ is isosceles.

18. Possible answer: Consider $\triangle ABC$ with altitudes $\overline{AD}$, $\overline{BE}$, and $\overline{CF}$. Because the shortest distance from a point to a line is the perpendicular, $AD < AB$, $BE < BC$, and $CF < AC$. So, $AD + BE + CF < AB + BC + AC$. The sum of the altitudes is less than the perimeter.

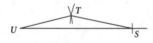

LESSON 4.4 · Are There Congruence Shortcuts?

1. Only one triangle because of SSS.

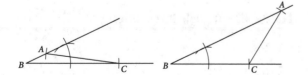

2. Two possible triangles.

3. Only one triangle because of SAS.

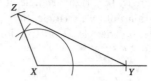

4. SAA or ASA   **5.** SSS   **6.** SSS

7. $\triangle BQM$ (SAS)   **8.** $\triangle TIE$ (SSS)

9. Cannot be determined   **10.** $\triangle TNO$ (SAS)

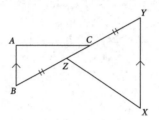

11. Cannot be determined   **12.** $D(9, 9)$, $G(3, 11)$

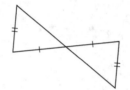

LESSON 4.5 · Are There Other Congruence Shortcuts?

1. All triangles will be congruent by ASA. Possible triangle:

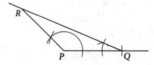

2. All triangles will be congruent by SAA. Possible procedure: Use $\angle A$ and $\angle C$ to construct $\angle B$ and then to copy $\angle A$ and $\angle B$ at the ends of $\overline{AB}$.

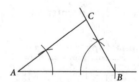

3. Cannot be determined

4. $\triangle XZY$ (SAA)   **5.** $\triangle ACB$ (ASA or SAA)

6. $\triangle PRS$ (SAA)   **7.** $\triangle NRA$ (SAA)

8. $\triangle GQK$ (ASA or SAA)

9. △ABE ≅ △DEB (ASA or SAA); △DEB ≅ △BCD (ASA or SAA); △ABE ≅ △BCD (Both are congruent to △DEB.)

10. Q(18, 9), R(20, −7). Slope $\overline{BC}$ = −8 and slope $\overline{QR}$ = −8. They have the same slope so they are parallel.

LESSON 4.6 · Corresponding Parts of Congruent Triangles

1. SSS, SAS, ASA, SAA

2. Third Angle Conjecture (or CPCTC after SAA)

3. Triangles are congruent by SAA. $\overline{BC}$ and $\overline{QR}$ are corresponding parts of congruent triangles.

4. AIA Conjecture   **5.** AIA Conjecture

6. ASA   **7.** CPCTC

8. △YWM ≅ △ZXM by SAS. $\overline{YW}$ ≅ $\overline{ZX}$ by CPCTC.

9. △ACD ≅ △BCD by SAS. $\overline{AD}$ ≅ $\overline{BD}$ by CPCTC.

10. Possible answer: DE and CF are both the distance between $\overleftrightarrow{DC}$ and $\overleftrightarrow{AB}$. Because the lines are parallel, the distances are equal. So, $\overline{DE}$ ≅ $\overline{CF}$.

11. Possible answer: $\overline{DE}$ ≅ $\overline{CF}$ (see Exercise 10). ∠DEF ≅ ∠CFE because both are right angles, $\overline{EF}$ ≅ $\overline{FE}$ because they are the same segments. So, △DEF ≅ △CFE by SAS. $\overline{EC}$ ≅ $\overline{FD}$ by CPCTC.

12. Possible answer: Because TP = RA and ∠PTR ≅ ∠ART are given and $\overline{TR}$ ≅ $\overline{RT}$, being the same segment, △PTR ≅ ∠ART by SAS and $\overline{TA}$ ≅ $\overline{RP}$ by CPCTC.

LESSON 4.7 · Flowchart Thinking

1. (See flowchart proof at bottom of page.)

2. (See flowchart proof at bottom of page.)

3. (See flowchart proof at bottom of page.)

LESSON 4.8 · Proving Isosceles Triangle Conjectures

1. AD = 8   **2.** m∠ACD = 36°

3. m∠B = 71°, CB = $19\frac{1}{2}$ **4.** m∠E = 60°

5. AN = 17   **6.** Perimeter ABCD = 104

Lesson 4.7, Exercises 1, 2, 3

1.

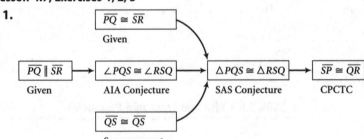

2.

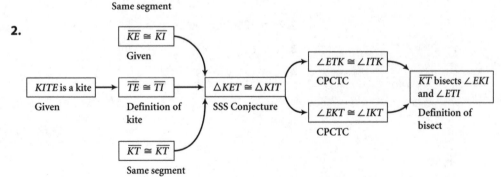

3.

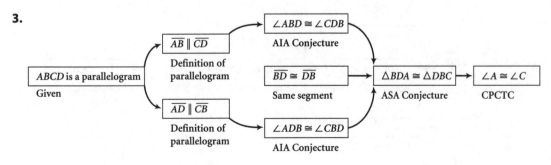

7. (See flowchart proof at bottom of page.)

8. Given: Isosceles △ABC
with $\overline{AC} \cong \overline{BC}$ and
median $\overline{CD}$

Show: $\overline{CD}$ bisects ∠ACB

Flowchart Proof

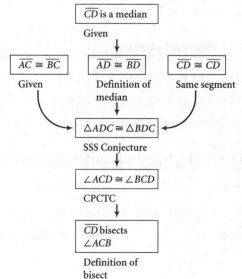

$\boxed{\overline{CD} \text{ is a median}}$
Given

$\boxed{\overline{AC} \cong \overline{BC}}$ $\boxed{\overline{AD} \cong \overline{BD}}$ $\boxed{\overline{CD} \cong \overline{CD}}$
Given   Definition of   Same segment
                    median

$\boxed{△ADC \cong △BDC}$
SSS Conjecture

$\boxed{∠ACD \cong ∠BCD}$
CPCTC

$\boxed{\overline{CD} \text{ bisects } ∠ACB}$
Definition of
bisect

LESSON 5.1 • Polygon Sum Conjecture

1. $a = 103°$, $b = 103°$, $c = 97°$, $d = 83°$, $e = 154°$

2. $x = 121.7°$, $y = 130°$

3. $p = 172°$, $q = 116°$, $r = 137°$, $s = 90°$, $t = 135°$

4. $a = 92°$, $b = 44°$, $c = 51°$, $d = 85°$, $e = 44°$,
$f = 136°$

5. $m∠E = 150°$

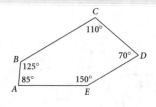

6. 170°; 36 sides   **7.** 15 sides

8. $x = 105°$ **9.** $x = 105°$

10. $x = 18°$ **11.** $m∠HFD = 147°$

LESSON 5.2 • Exterior Angles of a Polygon

1. $a = 64°$, $b = 138\frac{2}{3}°$ **2.** $a = 102°$, $b = 9°$

3. $a = 156°$, $b = 132°$, $c = 108°$

4. 12 sides   **5.** 24 sides

6. 4 sides   **7.** 6 sides

8. $m∠TXS = 30°$, $m∠SXP = 18°$, $m∠PXH = 12°$,
$m∠HXO = 15°$, $m∠OXY = 45°$

9. Each exterior angle is cut in half.

10. $a = 135°$, $b = 40°$, $c = 105°$, $d = 135°$

11.

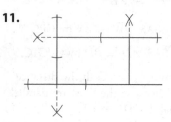

12.

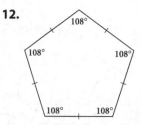

LESSON 5.3 • Kite and Trapezoid Properties

1. $x = 30$

2. $x = 124°$, $y = 56°$

3. $x = 64°$, $y = 43°$

4. $x = 12°$, $y = 49°$

Lesson 4.8, Exercise 7

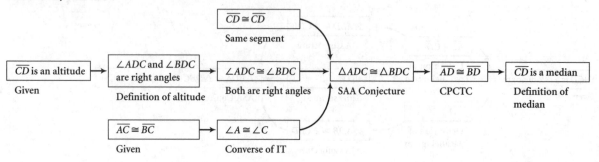

$\boxed{\overline{CD} \cong \overline{CD}}$
Same segment

$\boxed{\overline{CD} \text{ is an altitude}}$ → $\boxed{∠ADC \text{ and } ∠BDC \text{ are right angles}}$ → $\boxed{∠ADC \cong ∠BDC}$ → $\boxed{△ADC \cong △BDC}$ → $\boxed{\overline{AD} \cong \overline{BD}}$ → $\boxed{\overline{CD} \text{ is a median}}$
Given   Definition of altitude   Both are right angles   SAA Conjecture   CPCTC   Definition of median

$\boxed{\overline{AC} \cong \overline{BC}}$ → $\boxed{∠A \cong ∠C}$
Given   Converse of IT

Discovering Geometry Practice Your Skills
©2003 Key Curriculum Press

4. Flowchart Proof

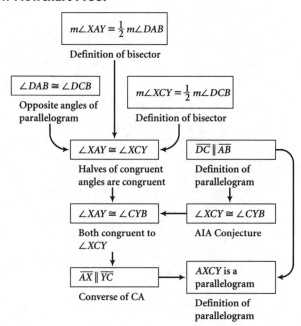

5. Flowchart Proof

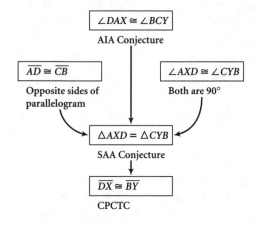

LESSON 6.1 · Chord Properties

1. $x = 16$ cm, y cannot be determined

2. v cannot be determined, $w = 90°$

3. $z = 45°$

4. $w = 100°$, $x = 50°$, $y = 110°$

5. $w = 49°$, $x = 122.5°$, $y = 65.5°$

6. kite. Possible explanation: $\overline{OM} \cong \overline{ON}$ because congruent chords $\overline{AB}$ and $\overline{AC}$ are the same distance from the center. $\overline{AM} \cong \overline{AN}$ because they are halves of congruent chords. So, $AMON$ has two pairs of adjacent congruent sides and is a kite.

7. Possible answer: Fold and crease to match the endpoints of the arc. The crease is the perpendicular

bisector of the chord connecting the endpoints. Fold and crease so that one endpoint falls on any other point on the arc. The crease is the perpendicular bisector of the chord between the two matching points. The center is the intersection of the two creases.

8. $P(0,1)$, $M(4, 2)$ 9. B

10. $m\overarc{AB} = 49°$, $m\overarc{ABC} = 253°$, $m\overarc{BAC} = 156°$, $m\overarc{ACB} = 311°$

LESSON 6.2 · Tangent Properties

1. $w = 126°$ 2. $m\angle BQX = 65°$

3. a. Trapezoid. Possible explanation: $\overline{MP}$ and $\overline{NQ}$ are both perpendicular to $\overline{PQ}$, so they are parallel to each other. The distance from M to $\overline{PQ}$ is MP, and the distance from N to $\overline{PQ}$ is NQ. But the two circles are not congruent, so $MP \neq NQ$. Therefore, $\overline{MN}$ is not a constant distance from $\overline{PQ}$ and they are not parallel. Exactly one pair of sides is parallel, so $MNQP$ is a trapezoid.

b. Rectangle. Possible explanation: Here $MP = NQ$, so $\overline{MN} \parallel \overline{PQ}$. Therefore, $MNQP$ is a parallelogram. Because $\angle P$ and $\angle Q$ both measure 90°, $\angle M$ and $\angle N$ also measure 90°, as they are opposite $\angle Q$ and $\angle P$ respectively. Therefore, $MNQP$ is a rectangle.

4. $y = -\frac{1}{3}x + 10$

5.

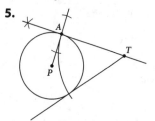

6. a. 4.85 cm   b. 11.55 cm

7. Possible answer: Tangent segments from a point to a circle are congruent. So $\overline{PA} \cong \overline{PB}$, $\overline{PB} \cong \overline{PC}$, and $\overline{PC} \cong \overline{PD}$. Therefore, $\overline{PA} \cong \overline{PD}$.

8. Possible answer: $\overline{PB} \cong \overline{PA}$ and $\overline{PC} \cong \overline{PA}$, so $\overline{PB} \cong \overline{PC}$. Therefore, $\triangle PBC$ is isosceles. The base angles of an isosceles triangle are congruent, so $\angle PCB \cong \angle PBC$.

1. $m\angle XNM = 40°$, $m\widehat{XN} = 180°$, $m\widehat{MN} = 100°$

2. $x = 120°$, $y = 60°$, $z = 120°$

3. $a = 90°$, $b = 55°$, $c = 35°$

4. $a = 50°$, $b = 60°$, $c = 70°$

5. $x = 140°$

6. $m\angle A = 90°$, $m\widehat{AB} = 72°$, $m\angle C = 36°$, $m\widehat{CB} = 108°$

7. $m\widehat{AD} = 140°$, $m\angle D = 30°$, $m\widehat{AB} = 60°$, $m\widehat{DAB} = 200°$

8. $p = 128°$, $q = 87°$, $r = 58°$, $s = 87°$

9. $a = 50°$, $b = 50°$, $c = 80°$, $d = 50°$, $e = 130°$, $f = 90°$, $g = 50°$, $h = 50°$, $j = 90°$, $k = 40°$, $m = 80°$, $n = 50°$, $p = 130°$

LESSON 6.4 • Proving Circle Conjectures

1. Construct $\overline{DO}$.

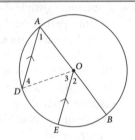

Flowchart Proof

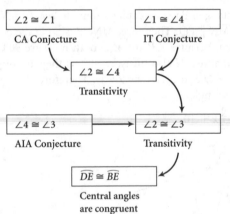

2. Flowchart Proof

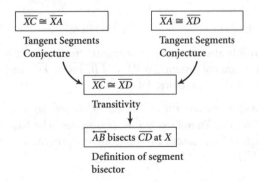

3. X is the intersection of $\overleftrightarrow{PQ}$ and $\overleftrightarrow{RS}$.

Flowchart Proof

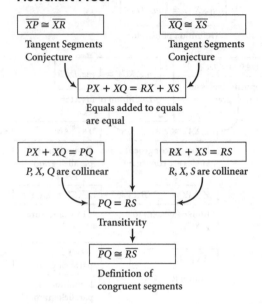

4. Possible answer:

Given: $ABCD$ is circumscribed about circle O. W, X, Y, and Z are the points of tangency.

Show: $AB + CD = BC + AD$

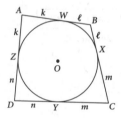

Paragraph Proof: $AW = AZ = k$, $BW = BX = \ell$, $CY = CX = m$, and $DY = DZ = n$ by the Tangent Segments Conjecture. So, $AB + CD = (AW + BW) + (CY + DY) = k + \ell + m + n$ and $BC + AD = (BX + CX) + (AZ + DZ) = \ell + m + k + n$. Therefore, $k + \ell + m + n = \ell + m + k + n$, so, $AB + CD = BC + AD$.

5. Given: $\widehat{AB} \cong \widehat{CD}$

Show: $\overline{AB} \cong \overline{CD}$

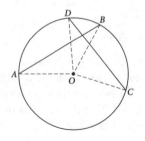

Flowchart Proof

Construct radii $\overline{AO}$, $\overline{OB}$, $\overline{OC}$, and $\overline{OD}$.

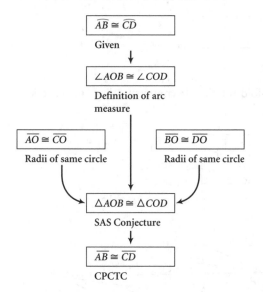

6. Given: $\overline{AB}$ and $\overline{CD}$ are chords that intersect at X. $\overline{AB} \cong \overline{CD}$.

Show: $\overline{AX} \cong \overline{CX}$ and $\overline{DX} \cong \overline{BX}$

Flowchart Proof

Construct $\overline{AC}$ and $\overline{BD}$.

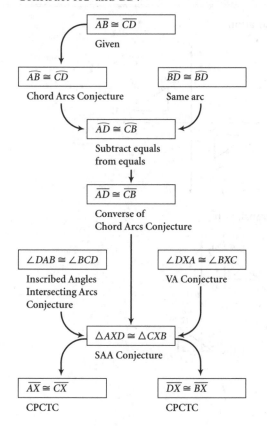

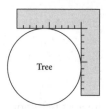

1. $C = 21\pi$ cm
2. $r = 12.5$ cm
3. $d = 9.6$ cm
4. $C = 12\pi$ cm
5. $C = 60\pi$ cm
6. $d = 24$ cm
7. $C = 2\pi\sqrt{2}$ cm
8. $C \approx 30.2$ cm
9. $C \approx 50.9$ cm
10. $d \approx 42.0$ cm, $r \approx 21.0$ cm
11. $C \approx 37.7$ in.
12. Yes; about 2.0 in.

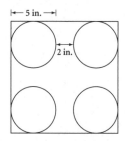

13. $C \approx 75.4$ cm
14. Press the square against the tree as shown. Measure the tangent segment on the square. The tangent segment is the same length as the radius. Use $C = 2\pi r$ to find the circumference.

15. 4 cm
16. 13.2 m

LESSON 6.6 · Around the World

1. At least 7 olive pieces
2. About 2.5 rotations
3. $\frac{(2\pi \cdot 4.23 \cdot 10^7)}{(60 \cdot 60 \cdot 23.93)} \cong 3085$ m/sec (about 3 km/sec or just under 2 mi/sec)
4. Each wrapping of the first 100 requires 0.4π cm, or 40π altogether. The next 100 wrappings require 0.5π cm each, or 50π altogether. Continue to increase the diameter by 0.1 cm.
   $40\pi + 50\pi + 60\pi + 70\pi + 80\pi + 90\pi + 100\pi$
   $= 490\pi$ cm ≈ 1539.4 cm ≈ 15.4 m.
5. 6.05 cm or 9.23 cm
6. Sitting speed $= \frac{(2\pi \cdot 1.4957 \cdot 10^{11}/10^3)}{(364.25 \cdot 24)}$
   $\approx 107{,}500$ km/hr

LESSON 6.7 • Arc Length

1. 4π **2.** 4π **3.** 30   **4.** $\frac{35\pi}{9}$

5. $\frac{80\pi}{9}$ **6.** 6.25π or $\frac{25\pi}{4}$ **7.** $\frac{100\pi}{9}$

8. 31.5   **9.** 22π **10.** 396

LESSON 7.1 • Transformations and Symmetry

1. 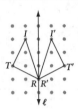   **2.**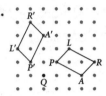

3.

4. Possible answers: The two points where the figure and the image intersect determine ℓ. Or connect any two corresponding points and construct the perpendicular bisector, which is ℓ.

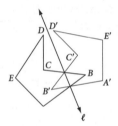

5. 3-fold rotational symmetry, 3 lines of reflection

6. 2-fold rotational symmetry

7. 1 line of reflection

8. 2-fold rotational symmetry, 2 lines of reflection

9. 2-fold rotational symmetry, 2 lines of reflection

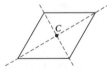

10. 2-fold rotational symmetry

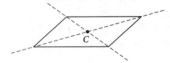

11. 1 line of reflection

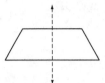

12. 4-fold rotational symmetry, 4 lines of reflection

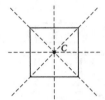

13.

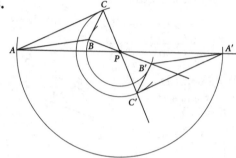

LESSON 7.2 • Properties of Isometries

1. Rotation

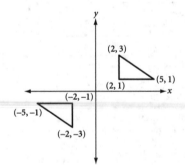

2. Translation

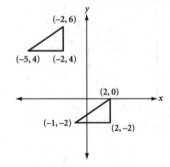

3. Reflection

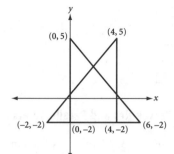

4.

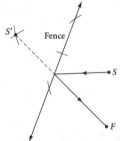

5.

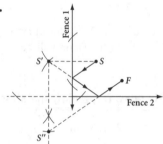

6. $(x, y) \rightarrow (x + 13, y + 6)$; translation; $B'(8, 8)$, $C(-8, -4)$

7. $(x, y) \rightarrow (-x, y)$; reflection over the y-axis; $P'(7, -3)$, $R(-4, 5)$

8. $(x, y) \rightarrow (y, x)$; reflection over the line $y = x$; $T'(7, 0)$, $R(0, 3)$

9. 1. $(x, y) \rightarrow (-x, -y)$; 2. $(x, y) \rightarrow (x + 4, y - 6)$; 3. $(x, y) \rightarrow (-x + 4, y)$; 6. $(x, y) \rightarrow (x - 13, y - 6)$; 7. $(x, y) \rightarrow (-x, y)$; 8. $(x, y) \rightarrow (y, x)$

LESSON 7.3 · Compositions of Transformations

1. Translation by $(-2, +5)$

2. Rotation 45° counterclockwise

3. Translation by $(+16, 0)$

4. Rotation 180° about the intersection of the two lines

5. Translation by $(-16, 0)$

6. Rotation 180° about the intersection of the two lines

7. Reflection over the line $x = -3$

8. Reflection over the line $x = 3$

9. $m\angle ROT = 50°$; rotation 100° clockwise about O

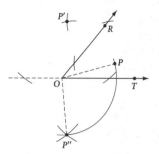

10. Translation 2 cm along the line perpendicular to k and ℓ

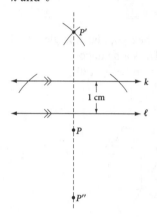

11.

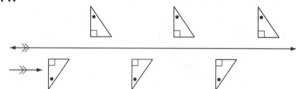

12.

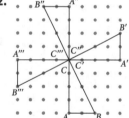

LESSONS 7.4–7.8 · Tessellations

1. $n = 15$ **2.** $n = 20$

3. Possible answer: A regular tessellation is a tessellation in which the tiles are congruent regular polygons whose edges exactly match.

4. Possible answer: A 1-uniform tiling is a tessellation in which all vertices are identical.

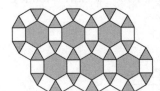

5.

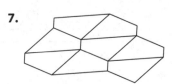

6. *ABCDEF* is a regular hexagon. Each angle measures 120°. *EFGHI* is a pentagon. $m\angle IEF = m\angle EFG = m\angle H = 120°$, $m\angle G = m\angle I = 90°$

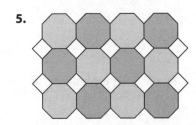

7.

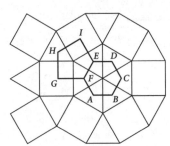

8. $3.4^2.6/3.6.3.6$

9. Sample answer:

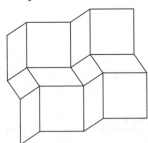

10. Sample answer:

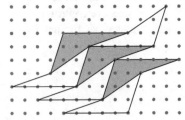

11. Sample answer:

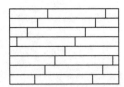

LESSON 8.1 • Areas of Rectangles and Parallelograms

1. 110 cm²   **2.** 81 cm²   **3.** 61 m   **4.** 10 cm

5. $98\frac{2}{3}$ ft, or 98 ft 8 in.

6. No. Possible answer:

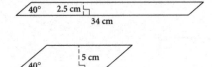

7. 88 units²   **8.** 72 units²

9. 737 ft   **10.** 640 acres

11. No. Carpet area is 20 yd² = 180 ft². Room area is (21.5 ft)(16.5 ft) = 206.25 ft². Dana will be $26\frac{1}{4}$ ft² short.

LESSON 8.2 • Areas of Triangles, Trapezoids, and Kites

1. 40 cm²   **2.** 135 cm²

3. $b = 12$ in.   **4.** $AD = 4.8$ cm

5. 123.5 cm²   **6.** $\frac{1}{16}$

7. Distance from *A* to $\overline{BC} \leq 6$ because the shortest distance from a point to a line is the perpendicular. Area using $\overline{BC}$ and this distance ≤ 27. Similarly, altitude from $B \leq 6$. So, area using base $\overline{AC} \leq 30$. Also, altitude from $C \leq 9$. So, again area ≤ 27. Combining these calculations, area of the triangle ≤ 27.

8. 48 in.²   **9.** 88 cm²

10. 54 units²   **11.** 49 units²

LESSON 8.3 • Area Problems

1. $1596.00

2. Possible answer:

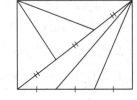

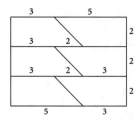

3. $18.75   **4.** 500 L

5. 40 pins: other diagonal is 6 cm; total rectangle area = 1134 cm²; area of 1 kite = 24 cm²; area of 40 kites = 960 cm²; area of waste = 174 cm²; percentage wasted ≈ 15.3%

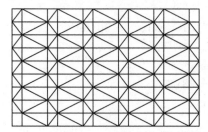

6. It is too late to change the area. The length of the diagonals determines the area.

LESSON 8.4 • Areas of Regular Polygons

1. $A ≈ 696$ cm²   **2.** $a ≈ 7.8$ cm

3. $p ≈ 43.6$ cm   **4.** $n = 10$

5. The circumscribed circle has diameter 16 cm. The inscribed circle has diameter ≈ 13.9 cm.

6. $s = 4$ cm, $a ≈ 2.8$ cm, $A ≈ 28$ cm²

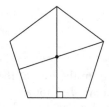

7. $s = 2.5$ cm, $a ≈ 3$ cm, $A ≈ 30$ cm²

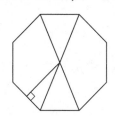

8. $s = 2$ cm, $a ≈ 3.1$ cm, $A ≈ 31$ cm²

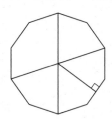

9. Possible answer: $s ≈ 3.1$ cm, $a ≈ 3.7$ cm, $A ≈ 45.9$ cm²

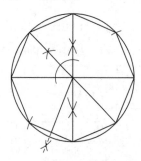

10. 31.5 cm²: area of square = 36; area of square within angle = $\frac{3}{8} \cdot 36 = 13.5$; area of octagon = 120; area of octagon within angle = $\frac{3}{8} \cdot 120 = 45$; shaded area = $45 - 13.5 = 31.5$ cm²

11. In trapezoid $ABCD$, $AB ≈ 5.20$ cm $(2.60 + 2.60)$, $DC ≈ 1.74$ cm $(0.87 + 0.87)$, and the altitude = 3 cm. Therefore, area $ABCD ≈ 10.41$ cm². In regular hexagon $CDEFGH$, $s ≈ 1.74$ cm, $a = 1.5$ cm. Therefore, area $CDEFGH ≈ 7.83$ cm².

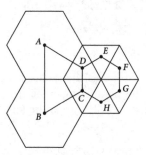

LESSON 8.5 • Areas of Circles

1. 10.24π cm²   **2.** 23 cm   **3.** 324π cm²

4. 191.13 cm²   **5.** 41.41 cm   **6.** 7.65 cm²

7. 51.31 cm²   **8.** 33.56 cm²   **9.** 73.06 units²

10. 56.25%   **11.** 78.54 cm² **12.** 1,522,527 ft²

LESSON 8.6 • Any Way You Slice It

1. 16.06 cm²   **2.** 13.98 cm²   **3.** 42.41 cm²

4. 31.42 cm²   **5.** 103.67 cm² **6.** 298.19 cm²

7. $r = 7.07$ cm   **8.** $r = 7.00$ cm

9. $OT = 8.36$ cm

10. 936 ft²

LESSON 8.7 • Surface Area

1. 136 cm²   **2.** 255.6 cm²   **3.** 558.1 cm²

4. 796.4 cm²   **5.** 356 cm²   **6.** 468 cm²

7. 1055.6 cm²   **8.** 1999.4 ft²

9. 1 sheet: front rectangle: $3 \cdot 1\frac{1}{2} = 4\frac{1}{2}$; back rectangle: $3 \cdot 2\frac{1}{2} = 7\frac{1}{2}$; bottom rectangle: $3 \cdot 2 = 6$; side trapezoids: $2\left(2 \cdot \frac{2\frac{1}{2} + 1\frac{1}{2}}{2}\right) = 8$; total $= 26$ ft². Area of 1 sheet $= 4 \cdot 8 = 32$ ft². Possible pattern:

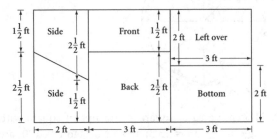

LESSON 9.1 • The Theorem of Pythagoras

1. $a = 21$ cm

2. $p = 23.9$ cm

3. $x = 8$ ft

4. $h = 14.3$ in.

5. Area $= 19.0$ ft²

6. $C(11, -1); r = 5$

7. 29.5 cm

8. Area $= 49.7$ cm²

9. $RV = 15.4$ cm

10. 6.4 cm

11. $SA = 121.3$ cm²

12. If the base area is 16π cm², then the radius is 4 cm. The radius is a leg of the right triangle; the slant height is the hypotenuse. The leg cannot be longer than the hypotenuse.

13. Area $= 150$ in.²; hypotenuse $QR = 25$ in.; altitude to the hypotenuse $= 12$ in.

14. 1.6 cm   **15.** 75.2 cm

LESSON 9.2 • The Converse of the Pythagorean Theorem

1. No   **2.** Yes   **3.** Yes   **4.** No

5. Yes   **6.** Yes   **7.** No

8. Yes. By the Converse of the Pythagorean Theorem, both $\triangle ABD$ and $\triangle EBC$ are right and in both $\angle B = 90°$. So $\angle ABD$ and $\angle EBC$ form a linear pair and A, B, and C all lie on the same line.

9. The top triangle is equilateral, so half its side length is 2.5. A triangle with sides 2.5, 6, and 6.5 is a right triangle because $2.5^2 + 6^2 = 6.5^2$. So the angle marked 95° is really 90°.

10. $x = 44.45$. By the Converse of the Pythagorean Theorem, $\triangle ADC$ is a right triangle, and $\angle ADC$ is a right angle. $\angle ADC$ and $\angle BDC$ are supplementary, so $\angle BDC$ is also a right triangle. Use the Pythagorean Theorem to find x.

11. 129.6 units²

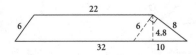

12. cannot be determined   **13.** No

14. cannot be determined   **15.** Yes

16. Yes

LESSON 9.3 • Two Special Right Triangles

1. $AC = 30\sqrt{2}$; $AB = 30 + 30\sqrt{2}$; area $= 450 + 450\sqrt{2}$

2. $AC = 30\sqrt{2}$; $AB = 30\sqrt{2} + 30\sqrt{6}$; area $= 900 + 900\sqrt{3}$

3. Perimeter $= 32 + 6\sqrt{2} + 6\sqrt{3}$; area $= 60 + 18\sqrt{3}$

4. $60.75\sqrt{3}$

5. Area $= \frac{1}{2}(p - r)^2 + rq$

6. $36.25\sqrt{3}$

7. $C\left(-\frac{1}{2}, \frac{\sqrt{3}}{2}\right)$

8. $C(-6\sqrt{3}, -6)$

9. Possible procedure: Construct a right triangle with one leg 2 units and the hypotenuse 4 units. The other leg will be $2\sqrt{3}$ units.

10. Possible procedure: Construct a right triangle with legs 1 unit and 2 units. Then construct a square on the hypotenuse. The square has area 5 units².

11. Area ≈ 234.31 ft²

LESSON 9.4 • Story Problems

1. The foot is about 8.7 ft away from the base of the building. To lower it by 2 ft, move the foot an additional 3.3 ft away from the base of the building.

2. About 6.4 km

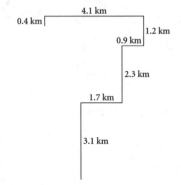

3. 149.5 linear feet of trim must be painted, or 224.3 feet². Two coats means 448.6 ft² of coverage. Just over $2\frac{1}{2}$ quarts of paint is needed. If Hans buys 3 quarts, he would have almost $\frac{1}{2}$ quart left. It is slightly cheaper to buy 1 gallon and have about $1\frac{1}{2}$ quarts left. The choice is one of money versus conserving.

4. 140° or 320°

LESSON 9.5 • Distance in Coordinate Geometry

1. Isosceles; perimeter = 32

2. $M(7, 10)$; $N(10, 14)$; slope $\overline{MN} = \frac{4}{3}$; slope $\overline{BC} = \frac{4}{3}$; $MN = 5$; $BC = 10$; the slopes are equal. $MN = \frac{1}{2}BC$.

3. $ABCD$ is a rhombus: All sides $= \sqrt{34}$, slope $\overline{AB} = -\frac{3}{5}$, slope $\overline{BC} = \frac{3}{5}$, so $\angle B$ is not a right angle, and $ABCD$ is not a square.

4. $PQRS$ is a rhombus: All sides $= \sqrt{82}$, slope $\overline{PQ} = 9$, slope $\overline{QR} = \frac{1}{9}$, so $\angle Q$ is not a right angle, and $PQRS$ is not a square.

5. $KLMN$ is a kite: $KL = LM = \sqrt{50}$, $MN = KN = 8$

6. $EFGH$ is a parallelogram: Opposite sides have the same length and same slope: $EF = GH = \sqrt{160}$; slope $\overline{EF}$ and $\overline{GF} = \frac{1}{3}$; $FG = EH = \sqrt{90}$; slope $\overline{FG}$ and $\overline{EH} = -\frac{1}{3}$

7. $WXYZ$ is a square: All sides $= \sqrt{145}$, slope $\overline{WX}$ and $\overline{YZ} = -\frac{9}{8}$, slope $\overline{XY}$ and $\overline{WZ} = \frac{8}{9}$, so all angles measure 90°.

8. $TUVW$ is an isosceles trapezoid: $\overline{TU}$ and $\overline{VW}$ have slope 1, so they are parallel. $\overline{UV}$ and $\overline{TW}$ have length $\sqrt{20}$ and are not parallel (slope $\overline{UV} = -\frac{1}{2}$, slope $\overline{TW} = -2$).

9. $(x - 0)^2 + (y + 3)^2 = 25$

10. The distances from the center to the three points on the circle are not all the same: $AP = \sqrt{61}$, $BP = \sqrt{61}$, $CP = \sqrt{52}$

11. $(-2, -4)$, $(6, 0)$, $(7, -7)$, $(8, -4)$, $(6, -8)$, $(7, -1)$, $(3, -9)$, $(0, 0)$, $(-1, -7)$, $(3, 1)$, $(0, -8)$, $(-1, -1)$

LESSON 9.6 • Circles and the Pythagorean Theorem

1. $CB = \sqrt{132} \approx 11.5$

2. Midpoint of chord $\overline{CA}$ is $H(6, 9)$. Slope $\overline{HT} = \frac{1}{4}$. This is not perpendicular to chord $\overline{CA}$, which has undefined slope.

3. $PT = \sqrt{88} \approx 9.4$; $PT^2 = 88$; $PS \cdot PQ = 88$. Sample explanation: $\triangle PTM$ is a right triangle, so

$$PT^2 = PM^2 - TM^2$$

$= (PS + SM)^2 - TM^2$	$PM = PS + SM.$
$= PS^2 + 2PS \cdot SM + SM^2 - TM^2$	Expand $(PS + SM)^2$.
$= PS^2 + 2PS \cdot SM + SM^2 - SM^2$	SM and TM are both radii.
$= PS^2 + 2PS \cdot SM$	Cancel SM^2.
$= PS(PS + 2SM)$	Factor out PS.
$= PS(PS + SQ)$	$2SM = SQ$ because $2r = d$.
$= PS \cdot PQ$	Because $PS + SQ = PQ$.

4. $\sqrt{5338} - 37 \approx 36.1$ cm

5. Area $= 56.57\pi \approx 177.7$ cm²

6. $AD = \sqrt{115.04} \approx 10.7$

7. $PR = \dfrac{8}{\sqrt{3}}$; $PB = \dfrac{16}{\sqrt{3}}$

8. $ST = 9\sqrt{3}$

9. $ST = 3\sqrt{35} \approx 17.7$

LESSON 10.1 • The Geometry of Solids

1. oblique   **2.** the axis   **3.** the altitude

4. bases   **5.** a radius   **6.** right

7. Circle C **8.** A **9.** $\overline{AC}$ or AC

10. $\overline{BC}$ or BC **11.** Right pentagonal prism

12. $ABCDE$ and $FGHIJ$

13. $\overline{AF}$, $\overline{BG}$, $\overline{CH}$, $\overline{DI}$, $\overline{EJ}$

14. Any of $\overline{AF}$, $\overline{BG}$, $\overline{CH}$, $\overline{DI}$, $\overline{EJ}$ or their lengths

15. False. The axis is not perpendicular to the base in an oblique cone.

16. False. In an oblique prism, the lateral edge is not an altitude.

17. False. A rectangular prism has six faces. Four are called lateral faces and two are called bases.

18. False. In order for a polyhedron to be a regular polyhedron, all faces must be regular polygons and also congruent to each other.

19. False. Only the bases are trapezoids. The lateral faces are rectangles or parallelograms.

20. tetrahedron   **21.** cube   **22.** heptahedron

23. height   **24.** lateral face

LESSON 10.2 · Volume of Prisms and Cylinders

1. 232.16 cm^3
2. 144 cm^3
3. 415.69 cm^3
4. $V = 8x^2y + 12xy$
5. $V = \frac{1}{4}p^2h\pi$
6. $V = \left(6 + \frac{1}{2}\pi\right)x^2y$
7. 6 ft^3
8. 30.77 yd^3

LESSON 10.3 · Volume of Pyramids and Cones

1. 80 cm^3
2. 209.14 cm^3
3. 615.75 cm^3
4. $V = 840x^3$
5. $V = \frac{8}{3}\pi a^2b$
6. $V = 4\pi xy^2$
7. B
8. C
9. C
10. B

LESSON 10.4 · Volume Problems

1. $6\sqrt{17}$ cm
2. 6.93 ft
3. 0.39 in.^{3}. Possible method: 120 sheets make a stack 0.5 in. high, so the volume of 120 sheets is 8.5 · 11 · 0.5 = 46.75 in.^{3}. Dividing by 120 gives a volume of 0.39 in.^{3} per sheet.
4. 24 cans; 3582 in.^{3} = 2.07 ft^3; 34.6%
5. 48 cans; 3708 in.^{3} = 2.14 ft^3; 21.5%
6. About 45.7 cm^3
7. 2000.6 lb (about 1 ton)
8. $V = \frac{8}{3}$ cm^3; $SA = (8 + 4\sqrt{2})$ cm$^2 \approx 13.66$ cm^2
9. About 110,447 gallons
10. 57 truckloads

LESSON 10.5 · Displacement and Density

1. 53.0 cm^3
2. 7.83 g/cm^3
3. 0.54 g/cm^3
4. 4.95 in.
5. No, it's not gold (or at least not pure gold). The mass of the nugget is 165 g, and the volume is 17.67 cm^3, so the density is 9.34 g/cm^3. Pure gold has density 19.3 g/cm^3.

LESSON 10.6 · Volume of a Sphere

1. 1150.3 cm^3
2. 12.4 cm^3
3. 785.4 cm^3
4. 318.3 cm^3
5. 11 cm
6. $10,666\frac{2}{3}\pi$ ft$^3 \approx 33,510.3$ ft^3
7. 4500π in.$^3 \approx 14,137.2$ in.^{3}

8. 1.5 cm
9. 497.4 units^3
10. 155.0 units^3
11. 823.2 in.^{3}; 47.6%
12. 17.86

LESSON 10.7 · Surface Area of a Sphere

1. $V = 1563.5$ cm^3; $S = 651.4$ cm^2
2. $V = 184.3$ cm^3; $S = 163.4$ cm^2
3. $V = 890.1$ cm^3; $S = 486.9$ cm^2
4. $V = 34.1$ cm^3; $S = 61.1$ cm^2
5. $457\frac{1}{3}\pi$ cm$^3 \approx 1436.8$ cm^3
6. About 3.9 cm
7. About 357.3 cm^2
8. About 1.38197
9. 163.4 units^2
10. 386.4 units^2
11. 9 quarts

LESSON 11.1 · Similar Polygons

1. $AP = 8$ cm; $EI = 7$ cm; $SN = 15$ cm; $YR = 12$ cm
2. $SL = 5.2$ cm; $MI = 10$ cm; $m\angle D = 120°$; $m\angle U = 85°$; $m\angle A = 80°$
3. Possible method: First, extend $\vec{PQ}$ and $\vec{PS}$. Then, mark off arcs equal to PQ and PS. Then, construct lines parallel to $\overline{QR}$ and $\overline{SR}$ to determine R'.

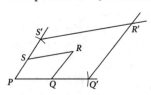

4. $QS = 3\sqrt{3}$ by the Pythagorean Theorem. But then by similarity $\frac{3}{6} = \frac{3\sqrt{3}}{8}$, which is not true.
5. Yes. All angle measures are equal and all sides are proportional.
6. Yes
7. No. $\frac{6}{18} \neq \frac{8}{22}$.
8. Yes
9. $\frac{D'A'}{DA} = \frac{R'T'}{RT} = 1.5$; Explanations will vary.

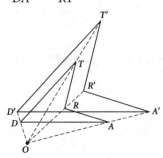

LESSON 11.2 • Similar Triangles

1. $MC = 10.5$ cm

2. $\angle Q \cong \angle X$; $QR = 4.84$ cm; $QS = 11.44$ cm

3. $\angle A \cong \angle E$; $CD = 13.5$ cm; $AB = 10$ cm

4. $TS = 15$ cm; $QP = 51$ cm

5. AA Similarity Conjecture

6. $CA = 64$ cm   **7.** $x \approx 18.59$ cm

8. Yes. By the Pythagorean Theorem the common side is 5. $\frac{3}{4} = \frac{3.75}{5}$ and the included angles are both right, so by SAS the triangles are similar.

9. $\triangle ABC \sim \triangle EDC$. Possible explanation: $\angle A \cong \angle E$ and $\angle B \cong \angle D$ by AIA, so by the AA Similarity Conjecture the triangles are similar.

10. $\triangle PQR \sim \triangle STR$. Possible explanation: $\angle P \cong \angle S$ and $\angle Q \cong \angle T$ because they are inscribed in the same arc, so by the AA Similarity Conjecture the triangles are similar.

11. $\triangle MLK \sim \triangle NOK$. Possible explanation: $\angle MLK \cong \angle NOK$ by CA, $\angle K \cong \angle K$ by identity, so by the AA Similarity Conjecture the two triangles are similar.

12. Any two of $\triangle IRG \sim \triangle RHG \sim \triangle IHR$. In each triangle, one angle is right, and each of the three pairs have a common angle. So, by the AA Similarity Conjecture, any pair of the three are similar.

13. Sample answer: $\triangle PXA \sim \triangle RXT$

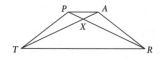

LESSON 11.3 • Indirect Measurement with Similar Triangles

1. 27 ft   **2.** 5 ft 4 in.   **3.** 6510 ft   **4.** 110.2 mi

5. 18.5 ft   **6.** 0.6 m, 1.2 m, 1.8 m, 2.4 m, and 3.0 m

7. Possible answer: The two triangles are roughly similar. Let O_1 be an object obscured by your thumb when you look through your left eye, and O_2 an object obscured by your right eye. Assuming you know the approximate distance between O_1 and O_2, you can approximate the distance from T to O_1 (or O_2). Here, it is about $10 \cdot TO_1$. (In most cases, 10 will be a pretty good multiplier. This can be a very convenient way to estimate distance.)

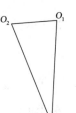

LESSON 11.4 • Corresponding Parts of Similar Triangles

1. $h = 0.9$ cm; $j = 4.0$ cm

2. 3.75 cm, 4.50 cm, 5.60 cm   **3.** 4.2 cm

4. $WX = 13\frac{5}{7}$ cm; $AD = 21$ cm; $DB = 12$ cm; $YZ = 8$ cm; $XZ = 6\frac{6}{7}$ cm

5. $AC = 10$ cm

6. Possible answer: Call the original segment $\overline{AB}$. Construct $\overrightarrow{AC'}$. Mark off 8 congruent segments of any length. Connect 8 to B and construct a parallel to $\overline{B8}$ through 3. C then divides $\overline{AB}$ into the ratio $3:5$.

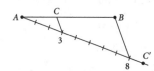

7. $x = \frac{50}{13} \approx 3.85$ cm; $y = \frac{80}{13} \approx 6.15$ cm

8. $a = 8$ cm; $b = 3.2$ cm; $c = 2.8$ cm

9. $CB = 24$ cm; $CD = 5.25$ cm; $AD = 8.75$ cm

LESSON 11.5 • Proportions with Area and Volume

1. Yes   **2.** No   **3.** Yes   **4.** Yes

5. $\frac{9}{25}$ **6.** $\frac{36}{1}$ **7.** $\frac{25}{4}$ **8.** $16:25$

9. $2:3$ **10.** $8:125$ **11.** $3:4$

12. $888\frac{8}{9}$ cm^2 **13.** 6 ft^2

LESSON 11.6 • Proportional Segments Between Parallel Lines

1. $x = 12$ cm   **2.** Yes

3. No   **4.** $NE = 31.25$ cm

5. $PR = 6$ cm; $PQ = 4$ cm; $RI = 12$ cm

6. $a = 9$ cm; $b = 18$ cm

7. $RS = 22.5$ cm, $EB = 20$ cm

8. $PE = 8.75$ cm, $QT = 6\frac{2}{7}$ cm

9. $x = 20$ cm; $y = 7.2$ cm

10. $x = \frac{\sqrt{97}}{3} \approx 3.28$ cm; $y = 5\frac{1}{3}$ cm

11. $p = \frac{16}{3}$ cm; $q = \frac{8}{3}$ cm

12. $x = 8.75$ cm; $y = 15.75$ cm

13. $AC = 5$ cm; $XY = 15$ cm. Possible explanation: $\overline{XY}$ divides $\overline{BC}$ and $\overline{BA}$ proportionately $\left(\frac{13}{26} = \frac{12}{24}\right)$, so $\overline{XY}$ is parallel to $\overline{AC}$. So, by CA, $m\angle YXB = 90°$.

LESSON 12.1 • Trigonometric Ratios

1. $\sin P = \dfrac{p}{r}$ **2.** $\cos P = \dfrac{q}{r}$ **3.** $\tan P = \dfrac{p}{q}$

4. $\sin Q = \dfrac{q}{r}$ **5.** $\cos Q = \dfrac{p}{r}$ **6.** $\tan Q = \dfrac{q}{p}$

7. $\sin T \approx 0.800$ **8.** $\cos T \approx 0.600$

9. $\tan T \approx 1.333$ **10.** $\sin R \approx 0.600$

11. $\cos R \approx 0.800$ **12.** $\tan R \approx 0.750$

13. $x \approx 12.27$ **14.** $x \approx 29.75$ **15.** $x \approx 149.53$

16. $x \approx 18.28$ **17.** $m\angle A \approx 71°$

18. $m\angle B \approx 53°$ **19.** $m\angle C \approx 30°$

20. $m\angle D \approx 22°$ **21.** $w \approx 18.0$ cm

22. $x \approx 7.4$ cm   **23.** $y \approx 76.3$ cm

24. $z \approx 11.1$ cm   **25.** $a \approx 28.3°$ **26.** $f \approx 12.5$ ft

27. $t \approx 11.9$ in.   **28.** $h \approx 34.0$ cm

29. apothem ≈ 4.1 cm, radius ≈ 5.1 cm

LESSON 12.2 • Problem Solving with Right Triangles

1. area ≈ 214 cm^2 **2.** area ≈ 325 ft^2

3. shaded area ≈ 36 cm^2 **4.** area ≈ 109 in.^{2}

5. $x \approx 54.0°$ **6.** $y \approx 31.3°$

7. $a \approx 7.6$ in.   **8.** diameter ≈ 20.5 cm

9. $\theta \approx 45.2°$ **10.** $\beta \approx 28.3°$

11. About 2.0 m   **12.** About 30.6°

13. About 202.3 newtons   **14.** About 445.2 ft

15. About 33.7°   **16.** About 22.6 ft

LESSON 12.3 • The Law of Sines

1. area ≈ 46 cm^2 **2.** area ≈ 24 m^2 **3.** area ≈ 45 ft^2

4. area ≈ 65 cm^2 **5.** $m \approx 14$ cm   **6.** $n \approx 37$ cm

7. $p \approx 17$ cm   **8.** $q \approx 13$ cm

9. $m\angle B \approx 66°$, $m\angle C \approx 33°$

10. $m\angle P \approx 37°$, $m\angle Q \approx 95°$

11. $m\angle K \approx 81°$, $m\angle M \approx 21°$

12. $m\angle STU \approx 139°$, $m\angle U \approx 41°$, $m\angle SVU \approx 95°$

13. $m\angle B \approx 81°$, $m\angle C \approx 40°$, area ≈ 12.3 cm^2

14. Second line: about 153 ft, between tethers: about 135 ft

15. About 6.0 m and 13.7 m

LESSON 12.4 • The Law of Cosines

1. $t \approx 13$ cm   **2.** $b \approx 67$ cm

3. $w \approx 34$ cm   **4.** $a \approx 39$ cm

5. $m\angle A \approx 76°$, $m\angle B \approx 45°$, $m\angle C \approx 59°$

6. $m\angle A \approx 77°$, $m\angle P \approx 66°$, $m\angle S \approx 37°$

7. $m\angle S \approx 46°$, $m\angle U \approx 85°$, $m\angle V \approx 49°$

8. 24°   **9.** About 43.0 cm

10. About 34.7 in.   **11.** About 492.8 ft

12. $l \approx 70.7$ ft   **13.** About 5.8 m, 139°

LESSON 12.5 • Problem Solving with Trigonometry

1. 2.85 mi/hr; about 15°

2. $m\angle A \approx 50.64°$, $m\angle B \approx 59.70°$, $m\angle C \approx 69.66°$

3. About 8.0 km from Tower 1, 5.1 km from Tower 2

4. a. $\cos A = \sqrt{1 - \sin^2 A}$ **b.** $\cos A \approx 0.7314$

5. About 853 miles

6. About 248 ± 30 ft, or 218 ft $< l <$ 278 ft where l is the length of the second shot

7. About 530 ft of fencing; about 11,656 ft^2

LESSON 13.1 • The Premises of Geometry

1. a. Given

  b. Distributive property

  c. Substitution property

  d. Subtraction property

  e. Addition property

  f. Division property

2. False

3. False

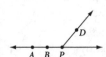

4. True; Perpendicular Postulate

5. True; transitive property of congruence and definition of congruence

6. *(See flowchart proof at bottom of page.)*

LESSON 13.2 · Planning a Geometry Proof

Proofs may vary.

1. Flowchart Proof

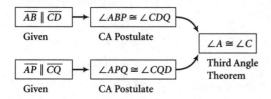

2. Flowchart Proof

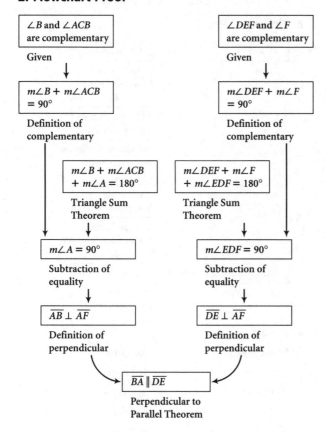

3. Flowchart Proof

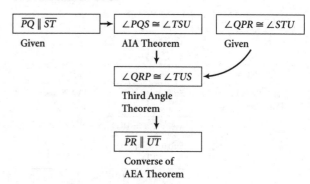

4. Flowchart Proof

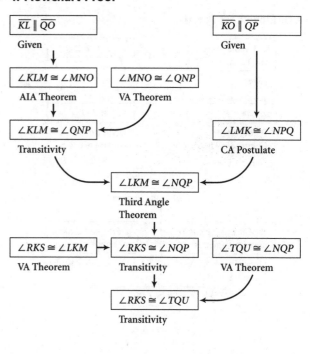

Lesson 13.1, Exercise 6

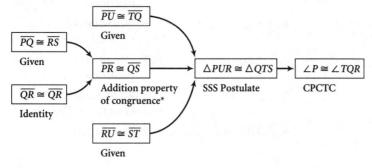

*Note: This step may require additional steps using the Segment Addition Postulate, definition of congruence, and transitive property of equality (or congruence).

5. Flowchart Proof

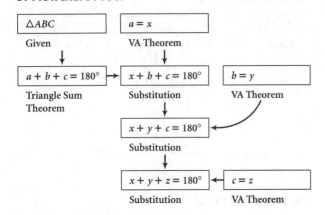

6. Flowchart Proof

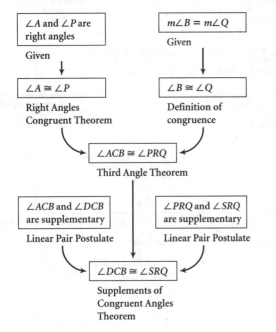

LESSON 13.3 • Triangle Proofs

Proofs may vary.

1. Flowchart Proof

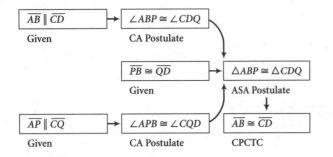

2. Proof:

Statement	Reason
1. $\angle BAC \cong \angle BCA$	1. Given
2. $\angle ABC$ is isosceles with $\overline{AB} \cong \overline{BC}$	2. Converse of IT Theorem

3. M and N are midpoints of $\overline{AB}$ and $\overline{BC}$	3. Given
4. $\overline{AM} \cong \overline{CN}$*	4. Definition of midpoint, Segment Addition Postulate, transitivity, algebra
5. $\overline{AC} \cong \overline{AC}$	5. Identity
6. $\triangle ACN \cong \triangle CAM$	6. SAS Theorem
7. $\angle ANC \cong \angle CMA$	7. CPCTC

*Note: This step could be broken into a series of steps showing that if two segments are congruent, then halves of each are also congruent.

3. Flowchart Proof

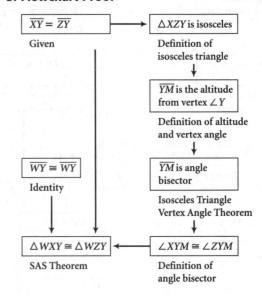

4. Proof:

Statement	Reason
1. $\overline{CD} \cong \overline{BD}$	1. Given
2. $\overline{BD} \perp \overline{AB}$	2. Given
3. $\overline{CD} \perp \overline{AC}$	3. Given
4. $\overline{AD}$ is bisector of $\angle CAB$	4. Converse of Angle Bisector Theorem
5. $\angle CAD \cong \angle BAD$	5. Definition of angle bisector
6. $\angle ACD$ is right	6. Definition of perpendicular
7. $\angle ABD$ is right	7. Definition of perpendicular
8. $\angle ACD \cong \angle ABD$	8. Right Angles Congruent Theorem
9. $\triangle ABD \cong \triangle ACD$	9. SAA Theorem

5. Flowchart Proof

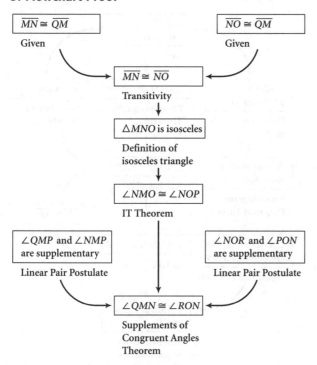

$\overline{MN} \cong \overline{QM}$
Given

$\overline{NO} \cong \overline{QM}$
Given

$\overline{MN} \cong \overline{NO}$
Transitivity

$\triangle MNO$ is isosceles
Definition of isosceles triangle

$\angle NMO \cong \angle NOP$
IT Theorem

$\angle QMP$ and $\angle NMP$ are supplementary
Linear Pair Postulate

$\angle NOR$ and $\angle PON$ are supplementary
Linear Pair Postulate

$\angle QMN \cong \angle RON$
Supplements of Congruent Angles Theorem

6. Flowchart Proof

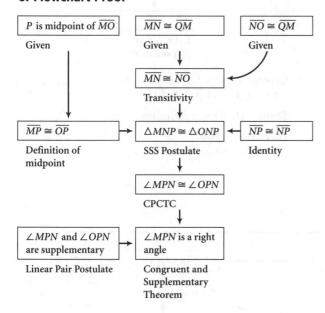

P is midpoint of $\overline{MO}$
Given

$\overline{MN} \cong \overline{QM}$
Given

$\overline{NO} \cong \overline{QM}$
Given

$\overline{MN} \cong \overline{NO}$
Transitivity

$\overline{MP} \cong \overline{OP}$
Definition of midpoint

$\triangle MNP \cong \triangle ONP$
SSS Postulate

$\overline{NP} \cong \overline{NP}$
Identity

$\angle MPN \cong \angle OPN$
CPCTC

$\angle MPN$ and $\angle OPN$ are supplementary
Linear Pair Postulate

$\angle MPN$ is a right angle
Congruent and Supplementary Theorem

7. Proof:

Statement	Reason
1. $\overline{AB} \cong \overline{BC}$	1. Given
2. $\triangle ABC$ is isosceles	2. Definition of isosceles triangle
3. $\angle A \cong \angle ACB$	3. IT Theorem
4. $\angle ACB \cong \angle DCE$	4. Given
5. $\angle A \cong \angle DCE$	5. Transitivity
6. $\overline{AB} \parallel \overline{CE}$	6. Converse of CA Postulate
7. $\angle ABD \cong \angle CED$	7. CA Postulate
8. $\overline{AB} \perp \overline{BD}$	8. Given
9. $\angle ABD$ is right	9. Definition of perpendicular
10. $\angle CED$ is right	10. Definition of right angle, transitivity
11. $\overline{BD} \perp \overline{CE}$	11. Definition of perpendicular

LESSON 13.4 • Quadrilateral Proofs

Proofs may vary.

1. Given: $ABCD$ is a parallelogram

Show: $\overline{AC}$ and $\overline{BD}$ bisect each other at M

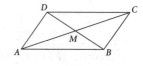

Flowchart Proof

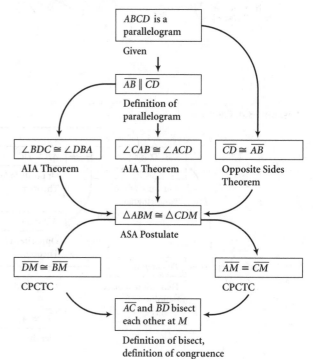

$ABCD$ is a parallelogram
Given

$\overline{AB} \parallel \overline{CD}$
Definition of parallelogram

$\angle BDC \cong \angle DBA$
AIA Theorem

$\angle CAB \cong \angle ACD$
AIA Theorem

$\overline{CD} \cong \overline{AB}$
Opposite Sides Theorem

$\triangle ABM \cong \triangle CDM$
ASA Postulate

$\overline{DM} \cong \overline{BM}$
CPCTC

$\overline{AM} = \overline{CM}$
CPCTC

$\overline{AC}$ and $\overline{BD}$ bisect each other at M
Definition of bisect, definition of congruence

2. Given: $DM = BM$, $AM = CM$

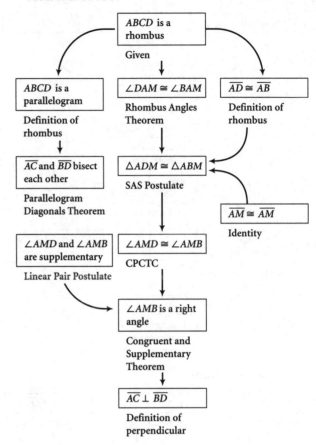

Show: $ABCD$ is a parallelogram

Proof:

Statement	Reason
1. $DM = BM$	1. Given
2. $\overline{DM} \cong \overline{BM}$	2. Definition of congruence
3. $AM = CM$	3. Given
4. $\overline{AM} \cong \overline{CM}$	4. Definition of congruence
5. $\angle DMA \cong \angle BMC$	5. VA Theorem
6. $\triangle AMD \cong \triangle CMB$	6. SAS Postulate
7. $\angle DAC \cong \angle BCA$	7. CPCTC
8. $\overline{AD} \parallel \overline{BC}$	8. Converse of AIA Theorem
9. $\angle DMC \cong \angle BMA$	9. VA Theorem
10. $\triangle DMC \cong \triangle BMA$	10. SAS Postulate
11. $\angle CDB \cong \angle ABD$	11. CPCTC
12. $\overline{DC} \parallel \overline{AB}$	12. Converse of AIA Theorem
13. $ABCD$ is a parallelogram	13. Definition of parallelogram

3. Given: $ABCD$ is a rhombus

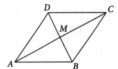

Show: $\overline{AC}$ and $\overline{BD}$ bisect each other at M and $\overline{AC} \perp \overline{BD}$

Flowchart Proof

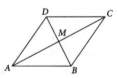

4. Given: $\overline{AC}$ and $\overline{BD}$ bisect each other at M and $\overline{AC} \perp \overline{BD}$

Show: $ABCD$ is a rhombus

Flowchart Proof

(See flowchart at bottom of page.)

Lesson 13.4, Exercise 4

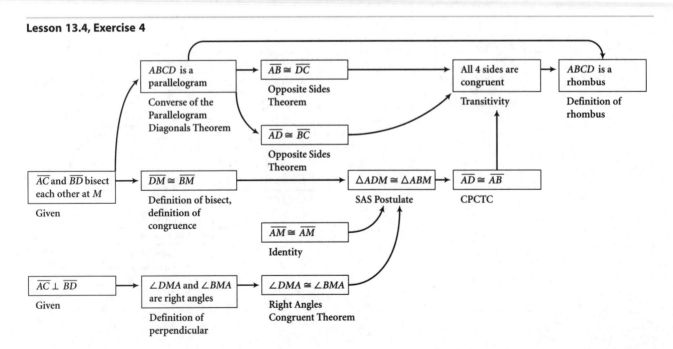

Discovering Geometry Practice Your Skills
©2003 Key Curriculum Press

5. Given: $ABCD$ is a trapezoid with $\overline{AB} \parallel \overline{CD}$ and $\angle A \cong \angle B$

Show: $ABCD$ is isosceles

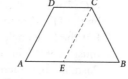

Proof:

Statement	Reason
1. $ABCD$ is a trapezoid with $\overline{AB} \parallel \overline{CD}$	1. Given
2. Construct $\overline{CE} \parallel \overline{AD}$	2. Parallel Postulate
3. $AECD$ is a parallelogram	3. Definition of parallelogram
4. $\overline{AD} \cong \overline{CE}$	4. Opposite Sides Congruent Theorem
5. $\angle A \cong \angle BEC$	5. CA Postulate
6. $\angle A \cong \angle B$	6. Given
7. $\angle BEC \cong \angle B$	7. Transitivity
8. $\triangle ECB$ is isosceles	8. Converse of IT Theorem
9. $\overline{EC} \cong \overline{CB}$	9. Definition of isosceles triangle
10. $\overline{AD} \cong \overline{CB}$	10. Transitivity
11. $ABCD$ is isosceles	11. Definition of isosceles trapezoid

6. Given: $ABCD$ is a trapezoid with $\overline{AB} \parallel \overline{CD}$ and $\overline{AC} \cong \overline{BD}$

Show: $ABCD$ is isosceles

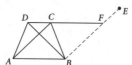

Proof:

Statement	Reason
1. $ABCD$ is a trapezoid with $\overline{AB} \parallel \overline{CD}$	1. Given
2. Construct $\overleftrightarrow{BE} \parallel \overline{AC}$	2. Parallel Postulate
3. $\overleftrightarrow{DC}$ and $\overleftrightarrow{BE}$ intersect at F	3. Line Intersection Postulate
4. $ABFC$ is a parallelogram	4. Definition of parallelogram
5. $\overline{AC} \cong \overline{BF}$	5. Opposite Sides Congruent Theorem
6. $\overline{DB} \cong \overline{AC}$	6. Given
7. $\overline{BF} \cong \overline{DB}$	7. Transitivity
8. $\triangle DFB$ is isosceles	8. Definition of isosceles triangle
9. $\angle DFB \cong \angle FDB$	9. IT Theorem
10. $\angle CAB \cong \angle DFB$	10. Opposite Angles Theorem
11. $\angle FDB \cong \angle DBA$	11. AIA Theorem
12. $\angle CAB \cong \angle DBA$	12. Transitivity
13. $\overline{AB} \cong \overline{AB}$	13. Identity

14. $\triangle ACB \cong \triangle BDA$	14. SAS Postulate
15. $\overline{AD} \cong \overline{BC}$	15. CPCTC
16. $ABCD$ is isosceles	16. Definition of isosceles trapezoid

7. False

8. True

Given: $ABCD$ with $\overline{AB} \parallel \overline{CD}$ and $\angle A \cong \angle C$

Show: $ABCD$ is a parallelogram

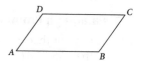

Flowchart Proof

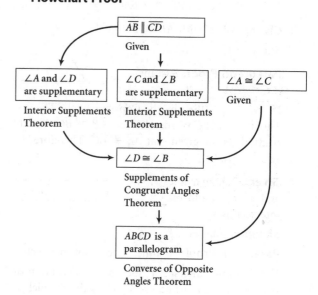

9. False

LESSON 13.5 · Indirect Proof

Proofs may vary.

1. Assume $BC \le AC$

Case 1: $\triangle ABC$ is isosceles, by the definition of isosceles. By the IT Theorem, $\angle A \cong \angle B$, which contradicts the given that $m\angle A > m\angle B$. So, $BC \ne AC$.

Case 2: $\triangle DBC$ is isosceles.

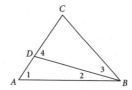

By the Exterior Angle Theorem, $m\angle 1 + m\angle 2 = m\angle 4$, so $m\angle 1 < m\angle 4$.

By the Angle Sum Postulate, $m\angle 2 + m\angle 3 = m\angle ABC$, so $m\angle 3 < m\angle ABC$. But $\triangle DBC$ is isosceles, so $m\angle 4 = m\angle 3$ by the IT Theorem.

So, by transitivity, $m\angle 1 < m\angle 4 = m\angle 3 < m\angle ABC$, or $m\angle 1 < m\angle ABC$, which contradicts the given that $m\angle A > m\angle B$. So $BC \not< AC$.

Therefore the assumption, $BC \le AC$, is false, so $BC > AC$.

2. **Paragraph Proof:** Assume $\angle DAC \cong \angle BAC$

It is given that $\overline{AD} \cong \overline{AB}$. By identity $\overline{AC} \cong \overline{AC}$. So by SAS, $\triangle ADC \cong \triangle ABC$. Then $\overline{DC} \cong \overline{BC}$ by CPCTC. But this contradicts the given that $\overline{DC} \not\cong \overline{BC}$. So $\angle DAC \not\cong \angle BAC$.

3. **Given:** $\triangle ABC$ with $\overline{AB} \not\cong \overline{BC}$

   Show: $\angle C \not\cong \angle A$

   Paragraph Proof: Assume $\angle C \cong \angle A$

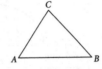

If $\angle C \cong \angle A$, then by the Converse of the IT Theorem $\triangle ABC$ is isosceles and $\overline{AB} \cong \overline{BC}$. But this contradicts the given that $\overline{AB} \not\cong \overline{BC}$. Therefore $\angle C \not\cong \angle A$.

4. **Given:** Coplanar lines k, ℓ, and m, $k \parallel \ell$, and m intersecting k

   Show: m intersects ℓ

   Paragraph Proof: Assume m does not intersect ℓ

If m does not intersect ℓ, then by the definition of parallel $m \parallel \ell$. But because $k \parallel \ell$, by the Parallel Transitivity Theorem $k \parallel m$. This contradicts the given that m intersects k. Therefore m intersects ℓ.

5. **Given:** Circle O with radius $\overline{OT}$ and $\overleftrightarrow{AT} \perp \overline{OT}$

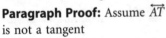

   Show: $\overleftrightarrow{AT}$ is a tangent

   Paragraph Proof: Assume $\overleftrightarrow{AT}$ is not a tangent

If $\overleftrightarrow{AT}$ is not a tangent, then $\overleftrightarrow{AT}$ intersects the circle in another point, S (definition of tangent).

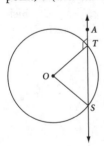

$\triangle OST$ is isosceles because $\overline{OT}$ and $\overline{OS}$ are radii. So, by the IT Theorem, the base angles are congruent. But the base angle at T is 90°, so the angle at S must be 90°. This contradicts the Perpendicular Postulate that there can be only one perpendicular from O to line $\overleftrightarrow{AT}$. So the assumption is false and $\overleftrightarrow{AT}$ is a tangent.

LESSON 13.6 · Circle Proofs

1. **Given:** Circle O with $\overline{AB} \cong \overline{CD}$

   Show: $\overarc{AB} \cong \overarc{CD}$

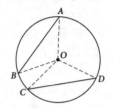

   Flowchart Proof

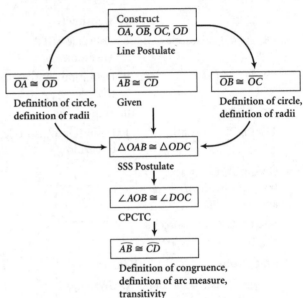

2. **Paragraph Proof:** Chords $\overline{BC}$, $\overline{CD}$, and $\overline{DE}$ are congruent because the pentagon is regular. By the proof in Exercise 1, the arcs $\overarc{BC}$, $\overarc{CD}$, and $\overarc{DE}$ are congruent and therefore have the same measure. $m\angle EAD = \frac{1}{2}m\overarc{DE}$ by the Inscribed Angles Intercepting Arcs Theorem. Similarly, $m\angle DAC = \frac{1}{2}m\overarc{DC}$ and $m\angle BAC = \frac{1}{2}m\overarc{BC}$. By transitivity and algebra, the three angles have the same measure. So, by the definition of trisect, the diagonals trisect $\angle BAE$.

3. The diagonals from one vertex of a regular n-gon divide the vertex angle into $n - 2$ congruent angles.

4. **Paragraph Proof:** Construct the common internal tangent $\overrightarrow{RU}$ (Line Postulate, definition of tangent). Label the intersection of the tangent and $\overline{TS}$ as U.

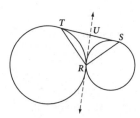

$\overline{TU} \cong \overline{RU} \cong \overline{SU}$ by the Tangent Segments Theorem. $\triangle TUR$ is isosceles by definition because $\overline{TU} \cong \overline{RU}$. So, by the IT Theorem, $\angle T \cong \angle TRU$. Call this angle measure x. $\triangle SUR$ is isosceles because $\overline{RU} \cong \overline{SU}$, and by the IT Theorem $\angle S \cong \angle URS$. Call this angle measure y. The angle measures of $\triangle TRS$ are then x, y, and $(x + y)$. By the Triangle Sum Theorem, $x + y + (x + y) = 180°$. By algebra (combining like terms and dividing by 2), $x + y = 90°$. But $m\angle TRS = x + y$, so by transitivity and the definition of right angle, $\angle TRS$ is a right angle.

5. **Given:** Circles O and P with common external tangents $\overline{AB}$ and $\overline{CD}$

   Show: $\overline{AB} \cong \overline{CD}$

   Paragraph Proof:

   Case 1: $\overline{AB} \parallel \overline{CD}$

   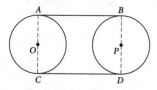

   Construct $\overline{OA}$ and $\overline{OC}$ (Line Postulate). $\angle OAB$ and $\angle OCD$ are right angles by the Tangent Theorem. By the Perpendiculars to Parallel Lines Theorem, $\overline{OA}$ and $\overline{OC}$ are parallel, but because they have O in common they are collinear. Similarly, $\angle CDP$ and $\angle ABP$ are right and B, P, and D are collinear. Therefore, by the Four Congruent Angles Theorem, $ABCD$ is a rectangle and hence a parallelogram. By the Opposite Sides Congruent Theorem, $\overline{AB} \cong \overline{CD}$.

   Case 2: $\overline{AB} \nparallel \overline{CD}$

   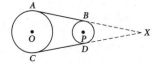

   Extend $\overline{AB}$ and $\overline{CD}$ until they intersect at X (definition of parallel). By the Tangent Segments Theorem, $XA = XC$ and $XB = XD$. By subtracting and using the Segment Addition Postulate $AB = CD$, or $\overline{AB} \cong \overline{CD}$ (definition of congruence).

6. **Given:** Circle O with chord $\overline{AB}$; $\overleftrightarrow{MN}$ is the perpendicular bisector of $\overline{AB}$

   Show: O is on $\overleftrightarrow{MN}$

   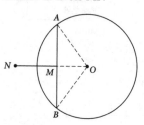

   Proof:

Statement	**Reason**
1. Construct $\overline{OA}$, $\overline{OB}$, and $\overline{OM}$	1. Line Postulate
2. $\overline{OA} \cong \overline{OB}$	2. Definition of radius
3. $\triangle OAB$ is isosceles	3. Definition of isosceles triangle
4. $\overleftrightarrow{MN}$ is the perpendicular bisector of $\overline{AB}$	4. Given
5. M is the midpoint of $\overline{AB}$	5. Definition of bisector
6. $\overline{OM}$ is the median of $\triangle OAB$	6. Definition of median
7. $\overline{OM}$ is the altitude of $\triangle OAB$	7. Vertex Angle Theorem
8. $\overline{OM} \perp \overline{AB}$	8. Definition of altitude
9. $\overleftrightarrow{MN} \perp \overline{AB}$	9. Definition of perpendicular bisector
10. O, M, and N are collinear	10. Perpendicular Postulate

7. **Paragraph Proof:** Construct tangent $\overleftrightarrow{TP}$ (Line Postulate, definition of tangent). $\angle PTD$ and $\angle TAC$ both have the same intercepted arc, $\overparen{TC}$. Similarly, $\angle PTD$ and $\angle TBD$ have the same intercepted arc, $\overparen{TD}$. So, by transitivity, the Inscribed Angles Intercepting Arcs Theorem, and algebra, $\angle TAC$ and $\angle TBD$ are congruent. Therefore, by the Converse of the CA Postulate, $\overline{AC} \parallel \overline{BD}$.

   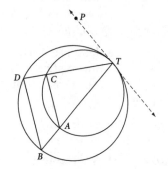

1. Flowchart Proof

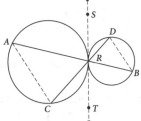

$\angle A \cong \angle BCD$	$\angle B \cong \angle B$
Given	Identity

$\triangle ABC \sim \triangle CBD$

AA Similarity Postulate

$\dfrac{AB}{BC} = \dfrac{BC}{BD}$

Definition of similar triangle

$BC^2 = AB \cdot BD$

Multiplication property

2.

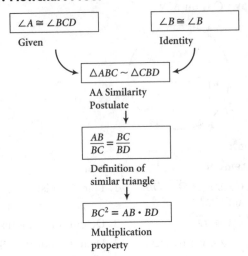

Proof:

Statement	Reason
1. Construct $\overline{AC}$ and $\overline{BD}$	1. Line Postulate
2. Construct common internal tangent $\overleftrightarrow{ST}$	2. Line Postulate, definition of tangent
3. $m\angle ARS = \frac{1}{2}m\widehat{AR}$	3. Inscribed Angles Intercepting Arcs Theorem
4. $m\angle ACR = \frac{1}{2}m\widehat{AR}$	4. Inscribed Angles Intercepting Arcs Theorem
5. $m\angle ARS = m\angle ACR$	5. Transitivity
6. $m\angle ARS = m\angle TRB$	6. VA Theorem, definition of congruence
7. $m\angle ACR = m\angle TRB$	7. Transitivity
8. $m\angle TRB = m\angle RDB$	8. Inscribed Angles Intercepting Arcs Theorem, transitivity
9. $m\angle ACR = m\angle RDB$	9. Transitivity
10. $\angle ACR \cong \angle RDB$	10. Definition of congruence
11. $\angle ARC \cong \angle DRB$	11. VA Theorem
12. $\triangle ACR \sim \triangle BDR$	12. AA Postulate
13. $\dfrac{AR}{CR} = \dfrac{BR}{DR}$	13. Definition of similarity

3. Proof:

Statement	Reason
1. $ABCD$ is a parallelogram	1. Given
2. $\overline{DC} \parallel \overline{AB}$	2. Definition of parallelogram
3. $\angle ECA \cong \angle CAB$	3. AIA Theorem
4. $\angle EFC \cong \angle AFB$	4. VA Theorem
5. $\triangle EFC \sim \triangle BFA$	5. AA Postulate
6. $\dfrac{EC}{AB} = \dfrac{CF}{AF}$	6. Definition of similarity
7. $CD = AB$	7. Opposite Sides Congruent Theorem
8. E is midpoint of $\overline{CD}$	8. Given
9. $EC = \frac{1}{2}CD$	9. Definition of midpoint
10. $EC = \frac{1}{2}AB$	10. Transitivity
11. $\dfrac{\frac{1}{2}AB}{AB} = \dfrac{CF}{AF}$	11. Substitution
12. $\frac{1}{2} = \dfrac{CF}{AF}$	12. Algebra
13. $AF = 2CF$	13. Multiplication property
14. $AF + FC = 2CF + FC$	14. Addition property
15. $AC = 3CF$	15. Segment addition property, algebra
16. $CF = \frac{1}{3}AC$	16. Division property

4. Given: Trapezoid $ABCD$ with $\overline{AB} \parallel \overline{CD}$ and $\overline{AC}$ and $\overline{BD}$ intersecting at E

Show: $\dfrac{DE}{BE} = \dfrac{CE}{AE} = \dfrac{DC}{AB}$

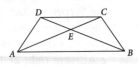

Flowchart Proof

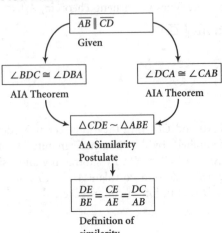

$\overline{AB} \parallel \overline{CD}$

Given

$\angle BDC \cong \angle DBA$	$\angle DCA \cong \angle CAB$
AIA Theorem	AIA Theorem

$\triangle CDE \sim \triangle ABE$

AA Similarity Postulate

$\dfrac{DE}{BE} = \dfrac{CE}{AE} = \dfrac{DC}{AB}$

Definition of similarity

Discovering Geometry Practice Your Skills
©2003 Key Curriculum Press

5. Given: $\triangle ABC$ with $\angle ACB$ right, $\overline{CD} \perp \overline{AB}$

Show: $AC \cdot BC = AB \cdot CD$

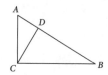

Flowchart Proof

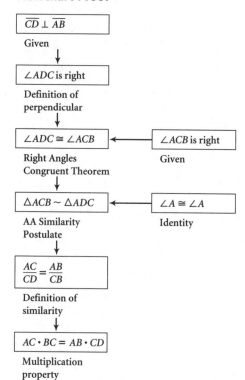

$\boxed{\overline{CD} \perp \overline{AB}}$
Given

$\boxed{\angle ADC \text{ is right}}$
Definition of
perpendicular

$\boxed{\angle ADC \cong \angle ACB} \longleftarrow \boxed{\angle ACB \text{ is right}}$
Right Angles   Given
Congruent Theorem

$\boxed{\triangle ACB \sim \triangle ADC} \longleftarrow \boxed{\angle A \cong \angle A}$
AA Similarity   Identity
Postulate

$\boxed{\dfrac{AC}{CD} = \dfrac{AB}{CB}}$
Definition of
similarity

$\boxed{AC \cdot BC = AB \cdot CD}$
Multiplication
property

6. Given: $ABCD$ with right angles A and C, $\overline{AB} \cong \overline{DC}$

Show: $ABCD$ is a rectangle

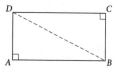

Proof:

Statement	Reason
1. Construct $\overline{DB}$	1. Line Postulate
2. $\angle A$ and $\angle C$ are right	2. Given
3. $\angle A \cong \angle C$	3. Right Angles Congruent Theorem
4. $\overline{AB} \cong \overline{DC}$	4. Given
5. $\overline{DB} \cong \overline{DB}$	5. Identity
6. $\triangle DBA \cong \triangle BDC$	6. HL Congruence Theorem
7. $\angle DAB \cong \angle BDC$	7. CPCTC
8. $m\angle DBA = m\angle BDC$	8. Definition of congruence
9. $m\angle ADB + m\angle DBA + m\angle A = 180°$	9. Triangle Sum Theorem
10. $m\angle A = 90°$	10. Definition of right angle
11. $m\angle ADB + m\angle DBA = 90°$	11. Subtraction property
12. $m\angle ADB + m\angle BDC = 90°$	12. Substitution
13. $m\angle ADB + m\angle BDC = m\angle ADC$	13. Angle Addition Postulate
14. $m\angle ADC = 90°$	14. Transitivity
15. $m\angle C = 90°$	15. Definition of right angle
16. $m\angle A + m\angle ABC + m\angle C + m\angle ADC = 360°$	16. Quadrilateral Sum Theorem
17. $m\angle ABC = 90°$	17. Substitution property and subtraction property
18. $\angle A \cong \angle ABC \cong \angle C \cong \angle ADC$	18. Definition of congruence
19. $ABCD$ is a rectangle	19. Four Congruent Angles Theorem